VOLUME FOUR

ADVANCING PSYCHOLOGICAL SCIENCE

ADVANCING PSYCHOLOGICAL SCIENCE

EDITED BY

Richard T. Louttit

RESEARCH
IN
PHYSIOLOGICAL
PSYCHOLOGY

WADSWORTH PUBLISHING COMPANY, INC.
Belmont, California

L.C. Cat. Card No.: 65–14315

Printed in the United States of America

PREFACE

In the Preface to the first three volumes of this series, Fillmore H. Sanford and E. John Capaldi introduced the strategy of employing a series of small volumes of readings in specific areas, so that an instructor may assign only those parts of the series that he considers most valuable to his students. To explain this strategy, they stated: "We felt that the student could neither fully understand nor properly appreciate psychology without digging deeply into at least a few substantive areas of concern. So we left the strategy of comprehensiveness to the textbooks, and selected materials . . . that stay with a single topic long enough and explore it in enough different ways to give the student, if he seeks it, some knowledge-in-depth in selected areas of psychological research."

The basic philosophy underlying the earlier volumes underlies this volume also. Guided by that philosophy, I have chosen three important areas of research in physiological psychology, areas of high interest value for most students, and have presented them in sufficient depth to give the student an understanding of (a) the ways in which the research has progressed, (b) some of the methodological problems of that research, and (c) the attempts of the researchers to integrate their empirical findings into meaningful theories.

Organized in this manner, this volume of research in physiological psychology will be of value not only to the beginning psychology student but also to the undergraduate studying physiological psychology. Graduate students may also benefit from studying the research problems presented here.

A short list of advanced reading suggestions is provided at the conclusion of each section, to allow the reader to follow a particular research problem further than space permits here. The Glossary and brain charts at the end will help the student follow the book without confusion over terms.

I would like to thank the following psychologists for their helpful comments and suggestions: Larry T. Brown, of Oklahoma State University; Thomas K. Landauer, of the Center for Advanced Study in the Behavioral Sciences, Stanford, California; Robert W. Lansing, of the University of Arizona; Lawrence I. O'Kelly, of the University of Illinois; and Mark R. Rosenzweig, of the University of California, Berkeley.

I wish to express sincere appreciation to the authors and publishers who so graciously allowed the reproduction of their work in this book. I hope that the greater distribution of their work will benefit the science of psychology. Finally, I wish to thank Mrs. Robert Sattler, whose efforts made completion of this volume possible.

Bethesda, Md.   R. T. L.

CONTENTS

INTRODUCTION

How do psychological processes work? What are the underlying mechanisms that motivate the individual organism? What mechanism is responsible for memory? How does the nervous system function in order to produce the behaviors that we observe in one another? It is such questions as these that physiological psychology attempts—tentatively—to answer.

The first section of these readings in physiological psychology deals with motivation: What mechanisms are necessary to motivate the individual to seek food or water, and how do these mechanisms operate? This section traces the development of research and thinking with regard to the cause of thirst. The early idea was that local dryness of the mouth and throat produced thirst, but current research uses direct chemical stimulation of the brain in order to locate specific brain areas involved in the production of thirst.

The second section deals with one of the most exciting research topics of recent years: How do we remember? Although this set of papers on memory covers only one decade, it lets the reader in on the excitement of discovery in science. No final conclusions are given, but the modes of research and theorizing are clearly demonstrated. The studies in this section focus primarily on the possibility that the molecular structure within brain cells serves as the basis for the storage of memory.

The third section presents recent research findings and theory derived from electrical self-stimulation of the brain. The impetus for study in this area was provided by a report in 1954, which indicated that rats can be motivated to learn a simple task in order to obtain the "reward" of having particular regions of their brains stimulated electrically. Since 1954, many laboratories have used this technique to study problems of motivation, attention, and learning in various organisms.

Included in this series of papers are studies using rats and studies using human patients. The findings are gathered together in a theory that indicates the existence of two opposing brain systems, one positive and the other negative. The balance of activity between these two systems is suggested as a factor in determining our behavior patterns.

RESEARCH
IN
PHYSIOLOGICAL
PSYCHOLOGY

1

MOTIVATION: THE PRODUCTION OF THIRST

Underlying much of human and animal behavior are biological, or primary, drives such as hunger and thirst. These and other motives, such as sex, temperature regulation, and the need for air, function homeostatically; that is, their purpose is to maintain a constant environment within the organism. Whenever an imbalance in this internal environment occurs, the organism (human or infrahuman) reacts. This reaction may be automatic (reflexive), or it may be learned. Such behavioral reactions are coordinated with internal physiological adjustments that are regulated through the endocrine system and the autonomic nervous system to restore balance to the internal environment. When we become cold, for example, our body temperature drops below the point of "balance," and we react with two sets of responses: (1) we automatically begin to shiver; (2) we seek a warmer room and warmer clothes—that is, we perform certain learned responses. Furthermore, we can observe this sort of behavior in everyday life. But the mechanisms, especially in the central nervous system, that produce the motives behind these responses are not so easily observed.

Thirst is one of the most important of our biological motives, and the past century of research and theory concerning thirst is an example of the development of scientific understanding with respect to all biological motives.

The first paper in this series is the noted physiologist Walter B. Cannon's presentation of a local theory of thirst. His talk, given to

1

the Royal Society of London in 1918 and slightly abridged here, reviews much of the early evidence for both a general theory of thirst and his own local theory. Two aspects of the evidence that supports his theory should be noted: (1) the use of anecdotal evidence (reports of individual instances); and (2) the use of the experimenter himself as the subject. These procedures have had great value in science, especially in the development of hypotheses that can be tested later by more rigorous techniques. Also, the reader should note the ever present possibility of researchers' interpreting the same data in different ways. The classic study of thirst that was carried out by Claude Bernard, one of the founders of experimental physiology, is an example. Cannon's interpretation of Bernard's data is clearly opposed to that of Bernard over half a century earlier.

THE PHYSIOLOGICAL BASIS OF THIRST*

Walter B. Cannon

In regarding the human body as a self-regulating organization, we observe that, so far as mere existence is concerned, it depends on three necessary supplies from the outer world—on food, to provide for growth and repair and to yield energy for internal activities and the maintenance of body heat; on oxygen, to serve the oxidative processes essential to life; and on water, as the medium in which occur all the chemical changes of the body. These three supplies are of different orders of urgency. Thus a man may live for thirty or forty days without taking food, as professional fasters have demonstrated, and suffer no apparent permanent injury to his bodily structure or functions. On the other hand, lack of oxygen for only a brief period may result in unconsciousness and death. Indeed, certain nerve cells in the cerebral cortex cannot withstand total deprivation of oxygen for more than eight or nine minutes without undergoing such fundamental changes that they do not again become normal when they receive their proper supply. Intermediate between the long survival without food and the very brief survival without oxygen is the period of existence which is

* Reprinted with minor modifications from *Proceedings of the Royal Society, London*, Series B, Vol. 90, 1918, pp. 283–301. By permission. Copyright © 1918 by the Royal Society.

possible without water. Records of men who have missed their way in desert regions and who, with no water to drink, have wandered in the scorching heat have proved that they rarely live under these circumstances of struggle and torrid atmosphere for more than three days, and many die within thirty-six hours. . . . If the thirsting man is not subjected to heat or exertion, his life may continue much longer than seven days. Viterbi, an Italian political prisoner, who committed suicide by refusing food and drink, died on the eighteenth day of his voluntary privation. After the third day the pangs of hunger ceased, but, until almost the last, thirst was always more insistent and tormenting. . . . Thus, though the period of survival varies, death is sure to come whether food, or oxygen, or water is withheld.

Normally these three supplies—food, oxygen, and water—are maintained in more or less constant adjustment to the bodily needs. Food material is being continually utilized in building body structure and in providing energy for bodily activities, but it is periodically restored. Oxygen is continually combining with carbon and hydrogen and leaving the body in CO_2 and H_2O, but the loss is compensated for with every breath. And water, likewise, is always being discharged in expired air, in secretion from the kidneys, and in sweat. So great is the escape by way of the lungs and skin alone that it is estimated that approximately 25 per cent of the heat loss from the body is due to evaporation from these surfaces. This continuous lessening of the water content must be checked by a new supply, or important functions will begin to show signs of need.

The evidence for the absolute necessity of water in our physiological processes requires no elaboration. Water is a universal and essential ingredient of all forms of organisms. Without it life disappears or is latent—the dry seed awakens only on becoming moist. . . .

Because water is a fundamental essential to life, and is continually escaping from the body, and because there is consequent need for repeated replenishment of the store, an inquiry into the mechanism of the replenishment is a matter of interest.

That such a mechanism exists is indicated by the fact that all our essential functions, leading to preservation of the individual and of the race, are controlled not through memory and volition, but by insistent sensations and desires. The unpleasant sensation of thirst causes us to drink. Not towards the subjective aspect of these automatic arrangements, however, is the special attention of the physiologist directed. He is primarily concerned with the bodily states which give rise to the sensation. Only when these states and their relations to the needs of the organism are known is the automatic control explained.

About six years ago I called attention to some graphic records of motions of the stomach in man which showed that the sensation of hunger is associated with powerful contractions of the empty or nearly empty organ. And because the hunger pang began to be experienced after the contraction had started, the conclusion was drawn that hunger is not a "general sensation," as was formerly held by physiologists and psychologists, but has its immediate origin in the stomach, and is the direct consequence of the strong contraction. This conclusion has since been abundantly confirmed by Carlson and his collaborators in observations on themselves and on a man with a gastric fistula.

Even more imperious than hunger as an insistent and tormenting sensation, accompanied by a dominant impulse which determines our behavior, is thirst. Indeed, these two experiences—hunger and thirst—are such impelling motives in directing our conduct that from early times they have been used as supreme examples of a strong desire. The ancient prophet spoke of a "hunger and thirst after righteousness" to express the eagerness of his yearning. And the common acquaintance of mankind with the potent demands of hunger and thirst for satisfaction renders these similes easily understood. . . .

There is a general agreement that thirst is a sensation referred to the mucous lining of the mouth and pharynx, and especially to the root of the tongue and to the palate. McGee, an American geologist of large experience in desert regions, who made numerous observations on sufferers from extreme thirst, has distinguished five stages through which men pass on their way to death from lack of water. In the first stage there is a feeling of dryness in the mouth and throat, accompanied by a craving for liquid. This is the common experience of normal thirst. The condition may be alleviated, as everyday practice demonstrates, by a moderate quantity of water, or through exciting a flow of saliva by taking into the mouth fruit acids such as lemon or tomato juice, or by chewing insoluble substances. In the second stage the saliva and mucus in the mouth and throat become scant and sticky. There is a feeling of dry deadness of the mucous membranes. The inbreathed air feels hot. The tongue clings to the teeth or cleaves to the roof of the mouth. A lump seems to rise in the throat, which starts endless swallowing motions to dislodge it. Water and wetness are then exalted as the end of all excellence. Even in this stage the distress can be alleviated by repeatedly sipping and sniffing a few drops of water at a time. "Many prospectors," McGee states, "become artists in mouth moistening, and carry canteens only for this purpose, depending on draughts in camp to supply the general needs of the system." The last three stages described by McGee, in which the eyelids stiffen over eyeballs set in a sightless stare, the distal tongue hardens to a dull weight, and the wretched victim has illusions of lakes and running streams, are too pathological for our present interest. The fact I wish to emphasize is the persistent dryness of the mouth and throat in thirst. . . .

Further evidence of the relation between local dryness of the mouth and throat and the sensation of thirst is found in some of the conditions which bring on the sensation. Breathing hot air free from moisture, prolonged speaking or singing, the repeated chewing of desiccated food, the inhibitory influence of fear and anxiety on salivary secretion, have all been observed to result in dryness of the buccal and pharyngeal mucous membrane and in attendant thirst. On the other hand, conditions arising in regions remote from the mouth and involving a reduction of the general fluid content of the body, such as profuse sweating, the excessive diarrhea of cholera, the diuresis of diabetes, as well as such losses as occur in hemorrhage and lactation, are well recognized causes of the same sensation. There appear to be, therefore, both local and general origins of thirst. In correspondence with these observations, two groups of theories have arisen, just as in the case of hunger—one explaining thirst as a local sensation, the other explaining it as a general, diffuse sensation. These theories require examination.

The view that thirst is a sensation of local origin has had few advocates, and the evidence in its favour is meagre. In 1885 Lepidi-Chioti and Fubini reported observations on a boy of 17, who, suffering from polyuria, passed from 13 to 15 litres of urine daily. When prevented from drinking for several hours, this youth was tormented by a most distressing thirst, which he referred to the back of the mouth, and at times to the epigastrium. The observers tried the effect of brushing the back of the mouth with a weak solution of cocaine. Scarcely was the application completed before the troublesome sensation wholly ceased, and the patient remained comfortable from fifteen to thirty-five minutes. If, instead of cocaine, water was used to brush over the mucous membranes, thirst was relieved for only two minutes. The temporary abolition of a persistent thirst by use of a local anesthetic, in a human being who could testify regarding his experience, is suggestive support for the local origin of the sensation. The evidence adduced by Valenti is also suggestive. He cocainized the back of the mouth and the upper esophagus of dogs which had been deprived of water for several days, and noted that they then refused to drink. One might suppose that the refusal to take water was due to inhibition of the swallowing reflex by anesthetization of the pharyngeal mucosa. . . . But Valenti states that his animals are quite capable of swallowing.

Though these observations are indicative of a local source of the thirst sensation, they leave unexplained the manner in which the sensation arises. Valenti has put forward the idea that all the afferent nerves of the upper part of the digestive tube are excitable to stimuli of thirst, but that suggestion does not advance our knowledge so long as we are left unenlightened as to what these stimuli are. A similar criticism may be offered to Luciani's theory that the sensory nerves of the buccal and pharyngeal mucosa are especially sensitive to a diminution of the water-content of the circulating fluid of the body; indeed, that these nerves are advance sentinels, like the skin nerves for pain, warning the body of danger. No special features of the nerves of this region, however, are known. No special end-organs are known. The intimation that these nerves are peculiarly related to a general bodily need is pure hypothesis. That they mediate the sensation of thirst is unquestioned. But the problem again is presented: How are they stimulated?

The view that thirst is a general sensation was well stated by Schiff. It arises, he declared, from a lessened water-content of the body, a condition from which the whole body suffers. The local reference to the pharynx, like the local reference of hunger to the stomach, is due to association of experiences. Thus the feeling of dryness in the throat, though it accompanies thirst, has only the value of a secondary phenomenon, and bears no deeper relation to the general sensation than heaviness of the eyelids bears to the general sensation of sleepiness. The conception of thirst, as a general sensation, is commonly accepted, and is supported by considerable experimental evidence. The interpretation of this evidence, however, is open to question, and should be examined critically.

First among the experiments cited are those of Dupuytren and the later, similar experiments of Orfila. These observers abolished thirst in dogs by injecting water and other liquids into the dogs' veins. . . . In these instances the treatment was no doubt general, in that it affected the body as a whole. But the assumption that thirst is thus proved to be a general sensation is unwarranted, for the injection of fluid into the circulation may have changed local conditions in the mouth and pharynx, so that the local sensation no longer arose.

A classic experiment repeatedly cited in the literature of thirst was one performed by Claude Bernard. He opened a gastric fistula which he had made in a dog, and allowed the water which the animal drank to pass out. As the animal became thirsty, it would drink until "fatigued," as the report states, and when "rested" it would begin again. But after the fistula was closed, drinking quickly assuaged the desire for water. The inference was drawn that thirst must be a general sensation, for the passage of water through the mouth and pharynx wet those surfaces, and yet the animal was not satisfied until the water was permitted to enter the intestine and be absorbed by the body. This evidence appears conclusive. The expressions "fatigued" and "rested," however, are interpretations of the observer, and not the testimony of the dog. Indeed, we may with equal reasonableness assume that the animal stopped drinking because he was not thirsty, and started again when he became thirsty. The only assumptions necessary for such an interpretation of the animal's behaviour are that appreciable time is required to moisten the buccal and pharyngeal mucosa sufficiently to extinguish thirst . . . and that these regions become dried rapidly when there is absence of an adequate water-content in the body. This interpretation is consistent with the view that thirst is a sensation having a local source. Furthermore, this interpretation is not contradicted by the satisfaction manifested by the dog after the fistula was closed, for the water which is absorbed, like that injected into veins, may quench thirst by altering local conditions. We cannot admit, therefore, that Bernard's experiment is proof that thirst is a general sensation.

Another set of observations cited as favourable to the theory of the diffused character of the origin of thirst are those of Longet. After severing the glosso-pharyngeal, the lingual and the vagus nerves on both sides in dogs, he observed that they drank as usual after eating. If thirst has a local origin in the mouth and pharynx, why should the animals in which the nerves to these regions were cut still take water? Two answers to this question may be given. First . . . Longet did not cut all branches of the vagi and trigemini to the mouth and pharynx, and, consequently, some sensation persisted. And second, even if all nerves were cut, the fact that the animals drank would not prove that thirst exists as a general feeling, for one may drink from the sight of fluid, or from custom, without the stimulation of a dry mouth, just as one may eat from the sight of food without the stimulus of hunger. . . .

The remaining evidence in favour of the diffused origin of thirst is found in studies of blood changes. These changes, by altering the "milieu intérieur" of the body cells, must affect them all. In 1900, Mayer published reports on the increase of osmotic pressure of the blood, as determined by depression of the freezing point of the serum, which he noted in conditions naturally accompanied by thirst. Dogs deprived of water for several days had a blood serum in which the osmotic pressure was increased, and rabbits kept in a specially warmed chamber showed the same change. Thus, conditions in which the water supply to the body was stopped, or the loss of water from the body by sweating or pulmonary evaporation was increased, either of which is known to cause thirst, were associated with a rise of osmotic pressure. And Mayer argued that all other circumstances in which thirst appears—in diabetes with increased blood sugar, in renal disease with accumulation of waste material in the body fluids, in acute rabies with total deprivation of water, in cholera with excessive outpouring of water into the intestine—the osmotic pressure of the blood would be augmented. Moreover, when a thirsty dog drinks, the hypertonicity of his serum disappears, his normal condition is restored, and he stops drinking.

By these observations Mayer was led to the conclusion that whenever the osmotic pressure of the blood rises above normal, thirst appears; whenever it returns to normal, thirst vanishes; and as the pressure varies, thirst also varies. Since intravenous injections of hypertonic salt solution cause, by stimulation of the bulbar centres, according to Mayer, a rise of arterial pressure and renal and intestinal vasodilation—both operating to lower the abnormally high osmotic pressure of the blood—he infers that other agencies are present in the organism, besides the desire for water, which tend to keep the blood normal. Thirst, he declares, is the last of a series of mechanisms acting to protect the organism against hypertonicity of its fluids.

In summary, then, the thirsty individual has a blood with high osmotic pressure. This condition affects all the cells of the body. It disturbs the cells of the central nervous system, and thus leads both to protective circulatory reactions and, in case these fail, to malaise and irritability, and a reference of unpleasantness to the region of the pharynx. Accompanying this, there is the impulse to drink, and when that is satisfied, the water taken in restores the normal state.

Mayer's observations were soon confirmed, but his inferences were challenged. In 1901, Wettendorff, working in Brussels, reported that if dogs are deprived of water, their blood does, indeed, develop a hypertonicity, as Mayer had found, but that this is a phenomenon which does not occur to any marked degree in the first days of the deprivation. In one instance there was no change in the freezing point of the serum during three days of thirst. Serious alteration of the osmotic pressure of the blood, therefore, is comparatively tardy in its appearance. Since the organism is continually losing water, and, nevertheless, the blood remains for a day or two unchanged, Wettendorff concluded that the consistency of the blood is preserved as long as possible by withdrawal of water from the extravascular fluids and the tissues. Further, thirst is clearly demonstrable long before any considerable change in the blood is evident. One animal, in which the freezing point of the serum had been lowered only 0.01° C. by four days' deprivation of water, drank 200 cc. of physiological salt solution, a liquid which to the dog in normal condition is quite repugnant. Again, when the blood has become slightly hypertonic, a dog may drink normal salt solution without lowering his osmotic pressure and afterwards, by refusing further drink, act quite as if he had slaked his thirst. But if an animal with a very hypertonic blood is placed before hypertonic salt solution he takes it again and again—an action which may be explained by a draining of water from the tissues with increasing intensity, and a consequent increasing thirst.

From all these observations Wettendorff concluded that the origin of thirst does not reside in alterations of the blood itself, but in the act of withdrawing water from the tissues. The liquids bathing the cells, therefore, would be first to concentrate as water is lost from the organism. And, since the conditions of cellular life would thus be modified in all the tissues, the peculiar state would develop which occasions the sensation of thirst. This effect is generally diffused, and is independent of any peculiar influence of the process of dehydration on the nervous system itself.

In accounting for the localizing of the sensation in the mouth and throat, Wettendorff distinguished between a "true thirst" and a "false thirst." "True thirst," he declared, is dependent on an actual bodily need, and is persistent until the need is satisfied. "False thirst" is only a dryness of the mouth and pharynx. Dryness in this region occurs, to be sure, in true thirst, but it is then an expression of the general dehydration of the tissues, exaggerated perhaps by contact with the outer air. Through experience the two conditions—buccal dryness and general dehydration—have become associated. Even in true thirst we may temporarily abolish the sensation by moistening the pharyngeal mucous membrane, but the result is only a "false satisfaction," a self-deception, made possible because long and pleasant experience has proved that moistening this region by drink leads to the satisfaction of an instinctive need.

The foregoing review of observations and theories has revealed that the attitude of physiologists with reference to thirst has been much as it was with reference to hunger. In each condition a general bodily need has arisen from a lack of essential bodily material and is signalled by a well-defined sensation. In each, the testimony of ingenuous persons regarding their feelings has been carefully set down, and then explained away. Thus in the case of thirst the primary sensation is described universally as an experience of dryness and stickiness in the mouth and throat. Instead of attempting to account for the experience as such, however, attention has been paid to the bodily need which accompanies it; apparently, since the need is a general one, the sensation has been supposed to be general, and the thirst which everybody experiences and knows about has been classed as an associated secondary phenomenon or the peripheral reference of a central change. The really doubtful feature in this view of thirst, just as in the older conception of hunger, is the "general sensation." That even the early stages of a need of water may be accompanied by increased irritability, and a vague sense of weakness and limpness, is not denied. But the thirsty man does not complain of these general conditions. He is tormented by a parched and burning throat, and any explanation of the physiological mechanism for maintaining the water content of the body must take into account this prominent fact.

In looking for a mechanism which would automatically keep up the water supply of our bodily economy, we may follow two clues; first, that there may be a peripheral arrangement which in the presence of a general bodily need for water would lead to dryness of the mouth and throat; and second, that a peripheral arrangement of this nature should be especially characteristic of animals which are constantly and rapidly losing water and require repeated renewal of the supply. These two clues offer a biological approach to the explanation of thirst which I wish to utilize.

In one sense, all animals are constantly losing water, for even in the simplest forms waste material is excreted in solution. With respect to water loss, however, we should expect to find a marked difference between animals living in water itself and those living in air. Indeed, it is difficult to conceive of an animal living in water as experiencing thirst. The entire body surface and the mouth and throat are throughout active life continuously bathed in a moving flow. The food is taken wet from a wet medium. Probably renal activity and the secretion of the digestive glands are the only important ways for water to leave the economy; and the digestive secretions are soon largely reabsorbed. In contrast, the land animals, mammals, for example, lose moisture not only in these ways but also by the moistening of dry food, by evaporation from the extensive surface of the lungs, and by the action of innumerable sweat glands. It is because of the possibility of great and rapid loss of water from its body that the land animal has special need for an assurance of adequate supply.

In the water inhabitant the skin, and the mouth and gullet, are all kept wet by the medium in which he lives and moves. In the process of evolution, however, as organisms changed their habitat from water to air, the skin became dry and scaly. Of the parts which in marine animals were constantly bathed by water, only the mouth and throat continue to be moist. These regions are now exposed to air, however, instead of being flushed by a flowing stream, and consequently they tend to dry. The structural lining of these parts probably renders them especially liable to desiccation in the presence of dry air, for the mucosa of the mouth and also of the pharynx, below the level of the floor of the nasal chambers, is composed of squamous epithelium. Some scattered mucous glands are present, but they are not capable of keeping the surfaces satisfactorily wet, as any one can readily prove by breathing through the mouth for only a few minutes. When air passes to and fro by way of this watercourse, as in prolonged speaking or singing, and in smoking, it is to be expected, therefore, that feelings of dryness and stickiness, which we call thirst, should arise.

Contrast this condition of the mouth with the condition of the respiratory tract, in which the lining membrane consists of columnar epithelium and is richly provided, particularly in the nose, with multitudes of mucous glands. Through this tract air moves to and fro constantly with no sign of inducing desiccation except in extreme and prolonged deprivation of water. But there is one portion of this normal pathway for the air which, in the absence of sufficient moisture, is peculiarly liable to become dried. It is the pharynx, where the respiratory tract crosses the digestive tract—i.e., where the inbreathed air, which may be insufficiently moistened in the nose, passes over surfaces of the ancient watercourse. Here, even with nasal respiration, unpleasant feelings may be excited, if the water-content of the body is reduced, and, in cases of marked thirst, the dryness of this region may stimulate tireless swallowing motions.

The central questions now appear: Why do not the mouth and pharynx feel dry and uncomfortable under normal conditions? and why do they feel so when the body stands in need of water? Again, a comparison of conditions in the water inhabitants, in which the buccal and pharyngeal regions are kept moistened by the surrounding medium, with conditions in the air inhabitants, in which these regions tend to be dried by the surrounding medium, will offer pertinent suggestions. A characteristic difference between these two animal groups is the possession, by the air inhabitants, of special buccal glands.

They are not present in fishes, but are found in the rest of the verte-brate series from the amphibia onwards. At first little differentiated, they develop in mammals into the three pairs of salivary glands—the parotid, sub-maxillary, and sub-lingual. For the purpose of consider-ing thirst in man, we may deal solely with this salivary group. The action of these organs is to secrete a fluid which is normally more than 97 per cent, and may be more than 99 per cent, water. The theory of thirst, on which I wish to offer evidence, may now be stated. In brief, it is that the salivary glands have, among their func-tions, that of keeping moist the ancient watercourse; that they, like other tissues, suffer when water is lacking in the body—a lack es-pecially important for them, however, because their secretion is almost wholly water; and that, when these glands fail to provide sufficient fluid to moisten the mouth and throat, the local discomfort and un-pleasantness which result constitute the feeling of thirst.

That one of the uses of buccal glands is to keep wet the surfaces over which their secretion is distributed is indicated by the fact that these structures first appear in air-inhabiting vertebrates. This indi-cation receives support from the conditions seen in the cetacea, the mammalian forms which have returned to an aquatic existence, and in which both the water-loss from the body and the need for wetting the mouth and throat are greatly reduced. It is a remarkable fact that in these animals the salivary glands are either lacking or are very rudimentary. The appearance and disappearance of the buccal glands in large animal groups, in correspondence with the exposure or non-exposure of the mouth and throat to desiccating air, point to these glands as protectors of the buccal mucosa against drying.

Experimental evidence as to the protective function of the salivary secretions was provided incidentally many years ago by Bidder and Schmidt. They were interested in studying any fluid secretion which might appear in the mouth apart from saliva. To this end they tied in dogs all the salivary ducts. The first effect was such a striking diminution of the fluid layer over the buccal mucosa that only when the mouth was held closed was the surface kept moist, and, when the animal breathed through the mouth, a real drying of the surface was hardly prevented. The eagerness for water, they state, was enormously increased, so that the animal was always ready to drink.

Related to this service of saliva in moistening and lubricating the mouth parts is the presence of a special reflex for salivary secretion when the buccal mucosa is exposed to conditions which tend to dry it. Thus, as Pavlov's researches demonstrated, with dry food in the mouth, much more saliva is secreted than with moist food. And

Zebrowski found, in the course of observations on patients with a parotid fistula, that, whereas no saliva flowed with the mouth closed, as much as 0.25 cc. in five minutes came from the duct when the mouth was opened. This reflex is readily demonstrated. If one closes the nostrils and breathes through the mouth for five minutes, usually nothing happens during the first minute. The mucosa then begins to feel dry, and at once the saliva starts flowing, and continues for the rest of the period. I have thus collected as much as 4.7 cc. in four minutes. Chewing motions, with the mouth empty, yielded in five minutes only about 1 cc. In these observations precautions were taken against any psychic effect due to interest by adding long columns of figures during the test. It seems clear, therefore, that if the mouth tends to become dry, the salivary glands are normally stimulated to action, and, if there is sufficient outflow from them, the affected surfaces are moistened. The act of swallowing favours the process, for the fluid is thereby spread backwards on the tongue and wiped down the back wall of the pharynx.

The question whether there is a relation between the existence of water-need in the body and diminished flow of saliva I have examined in two ways—by going without fluid for a considerable period, and by profuse sweating, combined with measurements of salivary secretion under uniform stimulation. The method of determining salivary output was that of chewing for five minutes at a uniform rate a tasteless gum, collecting the saliva which flowed during this period, and measuring its volume. All these observations are best made when one is inactive, and in my experience more nearly uniform results are obtained if one lies quiet during the tests.

The influence on salivary flow of going without fluid for some time may be illustrated by an example. The chewing to evoke salivary action was started at 7 o'clock in the morning, and repeated each hour until 8 o'clock in the evening. A breakfast consisting of a dry cereal preparation was taken between 8 and 9 o'clock, and a luncheon of dry bread between 12 and 1 o'clock. Nothing had been drunk since the previous evening. From the first test at 7 o'clock until 11 there was little change in the output of saliva; the average amount secreted in 5 minutes was 14.1 cc., with variations between 13 and 16.4 cc. Then the output began to fall, and at 2 o'clock only 6.4 cc. was secreted. The average amount for the two observations at 2 and 3 o'clock was 7.7 cc.—only little more than half that poured out in the morning. Between 3 and 4 o'clock a litre of water was drunk. The effect was soon apparent. At 4 o'clock the output was 15.6 cc., and during the next 4 hours, in which more water was taken, and a supper with thin soup and other fluid was consumed, the average amount secreted was 14.6 cc., a figure closely corresponding to the 14.1 cc. of the morning hours. . . . Other tests of this character gave similar results, though there was variation in the rate of decrease in the amounts of saliva secreted.

A similar diminution of the salivary secretion occurs after the loss of water from the body by sweating. In one instance, the loss in about one hour of approximately 500 cc. of body fluid as sweat was accompanied by a reduction in the salivary output of almost 50 per cent.

Corresponding to the diminution of the salivary output as the result of chewing was a diminution in the reflex flow as a consequence of letting the mouth become dry. The reflex flow has fallen, in my experience, from 3 or 4 cc. in five minutes under normal conditions to a little more than 1 cc. during thirst.

The relation between the decrease of salivary flow in these experiments and the sensation of thirst was quite definite. In the first experiment described, for example, the feeling of being "thirsty" was absent until the secretion of saliva began to decline, after 11 o'clock. From that time onward the back of the throat began to feel dry; there was frequent swallowing, and both the movements of the tongue and the act of deglutition were associated with a sense of "stickiness," a lack of adequate lubrication of the parts. All of this unpleasantness and discomfort disappeared after the restoration of the saliva flow by drinking water.

The increased spontaneous activity of the tongue and the repeated swallowing motions as "thirst" became more marked are noteworthy. These movements are a slight stimulus to salivary secretion, and they have, furthermore, the obvious effect of spreading about any fluid that might be present. In the absence of sufficient fluid, however, they augment the disagreeableness of the condition by making prominent the friction due to lack of lubricant. The "lump in the throat," which is complained of by persons who suffer from extreme thirst, can be explained as due to the difficulty encountered when the epiglottis and root of the tongue are rubbed over the dry back wall of the pharynx in attempts to swallow.

The only statement that I am aware of, which is contradictory to the evidence just presented, is that made by one of a group of psychologists, reported by Boring. This one observer testified that when he was beginning to be thirsty the saliva flow was still copious. The eight other observers of the group speak of thirst as being characterized by dryness of the roof of the mouth, dryness of the lips, the sensation of having a "dry sore throat," feelings of stickiness, and uncomfortable "puckery" pressure localized in the middle and back of the tongue and in the palate—in other words, as one of them summed up his experience, "dryness expresses the complex as a whole." This body of testimony agrees closely with that presented earlier and suggests that there may have been error in the one observation that thirst was associated with free secretion of saliva.

Other evidence on the relation between absence of saliva and the presence of thirst as a sensation was obtained through checking salivary secretion by atropine. Before the injection the amount secreted during 5 minutes by chewing averaged 13.5 cc. After the full effect of the drug was manifest, the amount fell to 1 cc. All the feelings that were noted in ordinary thirst—the sense of dry surfaces, the stickiness of the moving parts, the difficulties of speaking and swallowing—all were present. These disagreeable experiences, constituting the thirst sensation, disappeared as soon as the mouth and throat were washed out with a weak novocain solution. The immediate effect in these circumstances was doubtless due to the water in the solution, but since the relief lasted much longer than when water was used, the anesthetic was also a factor. This experience agrees with that of Lipidi-Chioti and Fubini, mentioned earlier. No water was drunk by me during the period of atropine effect, and yet when that effect disappeared, and the saliva flow was re-established, thirst also was abolished. The relation between thirst and such drug action has been noted before, but so strong has been the theory that thirst is a "general" sensation that the drug has been supposed to produce its effect not by local action but by central changes and by alteration of the blood. . . .

On the basis of the foregoing evidence I would explain thirst as due directly to what it seems to be due to—a relative drying of the mucosa of the mouth and pharynx. This may result either from excessive use of this passage for breathing, as in prolonged speaking or singing, or it may result from deficient salivary secretion. In the latter case "true thirst" exists, but it is not to be distinguished, so far as sensation is concerned, from "false thirst." True thirst is dependent on the fact that the salivary glands, which keep the buccal and pharyngeal mucosa moist, require water for their action. According to the observations and inferences of Wettendorff, the osmotic pressure of the blood is maintained, in spite of deprivation of water, by the withdrawal of water from the tissues. The salivary glands are included under "tissues," and they appear to suffer in a way which would support Wettendorff's view, for in the presence of a general need for water in the body, they fail to maintain the normal amount and quality of secretion. The same is doubtless true of other glands. The importance of this failure of action of the salivary glands, however, to the mechanism of the water supply of the body lies in the strategic position of these glands in relation to a surface which tends to become dry by the passage of air over it. If this surface is not kept moist, discomfort arises and with it an impulse to seek well-tried means of relief. Thus the diminishing activity of the salivary glands becomes a delicate indicator of the bodily demand for fluid.

The foregoing explanation is in agreement with the suggestions which have been offered to account for thirst as having a local origin. But it does not require specialized nerves, or peculiar sensitiveness of the first portion of the digestive tract, which have been assumed to be present by the upholders of this theory. And by calling attention to the arrangement by which the salivary glands are made to serve as indicators of the general bodily need for water, it presents a reasonable account of the manner in which a widespread condition of the organism may exhibit itself locally.

The experiments which have long been the chief support of the theory that thirst is a general sensation can also be explained by the evidence above adduced. The abolition of thirst by injecting fluid into the veins of thirsty animals would be expected, for, as shown in the experiment described above, by providing an adequate water supply the saliva flow is promptly re-established, and the parched mouth and throat are again continuously moistened. In the classic experiment of Claude Bernard, the animal with an open gastric fistula continued to drink until the fistula was closed. This was not because there was a general demand for water throughout the body, so long as the fistula remained open, but because only when escape through the fistula was stopped did the body receive the water needed to provide the output of saliva which prevented local drying. And the dogs with salivary glands tied, described by Bidder and Schmidt, were always ready to drink, just as are persons who are terrified or who have been given atropine, because of thirst—because there is local drying of the mouth—from lack of saliva, though the body as a whole may not be in any need of water. The application of cocaine to the mucous surfaces of the mouth abolishes the torment of thirst, not by any central effect, and clearly not by satisfying any general bodily requirement for water, but by rendering the surfaces anesthetic. The miraculous virtues of coca leaves as a balm for the distress of the thirsty, a fact long ago observed, is explicable on these grounds. The thirst of those who suffer from loss of fluid from the body—the diabetic patient, the victim of cholera, the subject of hemorrhage, the perspiring labourer, and the nursing mother—can be accounted for by the reduction of salivary flow as the water-content of the body is lowered, and by the consequent discomfort arising from the sticky buccal mucosa.

I am aware that many questions arising from the views which I have just developed remain to be solved—questions as to the effects which other glandular activity, removing fluid from the body, may exercise on the functions of the salivary glands; the alteration of properties of the blood and lymph other than osmotic pressure as affecting secretion; the relation between the so-called "free water" of the body fluids and salivary secretion when water is withheld; the influence of strong alcoholic beverages in producing thirst; and the nature of pathological states in which thirst seems to disappear. . . .

From the evidence presented, however, it seems to me that we are now in a position to understand the mechanisms by which all three of the essential supplies from the outer world are provided for in our bodily economy. The oxygen supply is arranged for by the control which changes in the blood, brought about mainly by variations in the carbon dioxide content, exert on the centre for respiration. The proper food supply ultimately is assured because we avoid, or check, by taking food, the distressing pangs of hunger which powerful contractions of the empty stomach induce unless food is taken. And the water supply is maintained because we avoid, or abolish, by taking water or aqueous fluid, the disagreeable sensations which arise and torment us with increasing torment if the salivary glands, because of a lowering of the water-content of the body, lack the water they need to function, and fail therefore to pour out their watery secretion in sufficient amount and in proper quality to keep moist the mouth and pharynx.

According to Cannon, changes in salivary secretions produce dryness in the mouth and throat, causing the sensation of thirst and the reaction of drinking. But, if dryness causes drinking, why do we not stop drinking after the first swallow? This question points up the importance of studying measurable behavior. The papers presented later in this section deal directly with thirst as it is demonstrated in water-drinking behavior under specified, controlled conditions.

What is the importance of the swallowing response? How does it operate to regulate drinking? The following article, by R. T. Bellows, a neurosurgeon, clearly demonstrates the importance of swallowing as a cue for regulation of drinking, but shows that the water content of the body is even more important.

TIME FACTORS IN WATER DRINKING IN DOGS*

R. T. Bellows

Thirst may be defined as the urge to drink water. The satisfaction of thirst is signified by the disappearance of the urge to drink. Much evidence has favored the view that thirst arises only from the local dryness of the mouth resulting from water privation (Cannon, 1933). More recent experiments, however, have indicated that this theory does not suffice to explain the phenomenon of thirst in all the conditions in which it may or may not exist. Dogs have been observed to refuse water although they revealed the external signs of desiccation, of dry mouth and loss of skin turgor (Darrow and Yannett, 1935). Thirst may occur when the mouth is wet: marine teleosts have been observed to drink their watery medium (Smith, 1930). Thirst may also appear in the absence of an absolute deficit of water; Gilman (1937) demonstrated thirst in dogs after the intravenous administration of hypertonic solutions. Dogs with diabetes insipidus and esophageal fistulae sham-drank persistently although there was no polyuria or loss of weight (Bellows and Van Wagenen, 1938).

Adolph (1939) has demonstrated that when deprived of water dogs will satisfy their thirst with a single draft of water in 5 minutes or less time, and that in doing so they will ingest accurately the amount of their deficit of water. It may thus be said that in the dog thirst is satisfied by a certain amount of water in the time required to ingest it. In the present investigation three series of observations were made on dogs with esophageal fistulae: *Series 1*. Correlation of the amounts and times of sham-drinking with real drinking. *Series 2*. Investigation of the time element in thirst satisfaction. *Series 3*. The amount and duration of sham-drinking which followed intravenous administration of hypertonic solutions were correlated with the diuresis and rate of solute excretion in the absence of real water ingestion.

Procedure

Two dogs were studied. The management of fistulous dogs has been described previously (Bellows and Van Wagenen, 1938).

* Reprinted from *American Journal of Physiology*, Vol. 125, 1939, pp. 87–97. By permission. Copyright © 1939 by the American Physiological Society.

They were regularly given two feedings daily of equal parts of whole dried milk and "fox chow."

In *series 1* and *2* the dogs were made to sham-drink by administering less than the normal requirement of water. At hourly intervals sham-drinking was permitted for a certain period of time or until the dog refused water for 5 minutes. The amount of water sham-drunk in each successive minute was recorded. In *series 1* a connecting tube, fitted for each dog, made of glass and rubber tubing, was inserted in the fistula to permit real-drinking instead of sham-drinking. This was done 1 hour after the previous sham-drink. In *series 2* the estimated water deficit plus a slight excess was administered by esophagus in 5 minutes. After intervals of variable lengths, sham-drinking was permitted. The administration of water equal to the deficit was timed so that the subsequent opportunity to sham-drink would be 1 hour after the previous sham-drink. In each test the water equal to the deficit was administered 5 to 7 hours after feeding.

Series 3. While in water balance and adipsic, the dogs were catheterized, weighed, and bled from the median basilic vein. They were given intravenously 2.5 cc/kgm of either 20 per cent NaCl or 40 per cent urea. Continuous sham-drinking was permitted immediately and recorded at 5 to 30 minute intervals for 6 or 8 hours and at the end of 24 hours. Urine samples were collected at longer intervals when voided or by catheterization, after each of which the animals were again weighed; 30 minutes after injection another blood sample was taken. Further samples were taken at intervals. At the end of 24 hours stools were collected and the cage was washed.

Chloride determinations were made on serum (Eisenman, 1929), urine, sham-drunk water, cage washings (Van Slyke, 1923), and stools (Birner, 1928). The urea of the urine, sham-drunk water, and cage washings was determined by the method of Folin and Youngburg (1919); of the serum and stools by the method of Folin and Wu (1919).

The normal feedings were given during the experiments of *series 3*. Dog B received the first feeding immediately before injection, the second 6 to 8 hours later. Dog C received the first feeding 6 hours after injection, the second 12 hours later. Food chlorides were determined by Birner's (1928) method. Total food nitrogen was calculated from the manufacturer's analysis.

The NaCl injection was repeated in each dog after 1 cc. of pitressin had been given subcutaneously 20 to 30 minutes before injection, and every 2 hours thereafter for 6 hours.

Results

General. When allowed to sham-drink intermittently during an unvarying deficit of water the fistulous dog sham-drank approximately the same amount of water every hour when the period of sham-drinking did not exceed 10 minutes. At 30-minute intervals the amount sham-drunk was usually but not always equivalent to the amount sham-drunk at hourly intervals. At intervals of less than 30 minutes the amount sham-drunk was variable; in general the shorter the interval the less was the amount sham-drunk. At intervals longer than 1 hour the amount sham-drunk did not exceed that at 1-hour intervals. Sham-drinking was constant then when the water deficit was constant and became maximal 30 to 50 minutes after a previous sham-drink.

The manner of sham-drinking was quite uniform in each dog. Dog B sham-drank continuously in one draft with only momentary pauses, after which the animal refused water for 10 or 15 minutes. Dog C sham-drank multiple short drafts of water, the pauses between drafts increasing in duration from 5 seconds to 2 or 3 minutes. Allowed to sham-drink for 30 minutes at 2-hour intervals this dog sham-drank ½ to ⅔ of the water in the first 10 minutes. Dog B sham-drank continuously twice as much water per minute as did dog C.

The rate of continuous sham-drinking did not change appreciably as the water deficit increased. Dog B slightly increased the rate of sham-drinking in the largest drafts. Dog C, on the other hand, slightly increased the rate in sham-drinking the smaller drafts. The quantity of water sham-drunk continuously at hourly intervals regularly increased as the deficit of water increased. Variations in the amount of sham-drinking from hour to hour appeared to be related to the feedings. When water privation was moderate, sham-drinking temporarily decreased after feeding. In more severe privation, feedings had little effect or temporarily increased sham-drinking.

The observations on dog B illustrate with especial clarity that (a) sham-drinking was proportional to the water deficit, and that (b) it apparently served to satisfy thirst temporarily.

Series 1. After the connecting tube was inserted the dogs were able to ingest the water they drank. This artificial restoration of the continuity of the esophagus proved as satisfactory as the natural esophagus in water drinking, for the dogs invariably terminated their privation when permitted to drink with the connecting tube. Water was drunk by dog B with the tube at the same continuous rate as it was sham-drunk. When large quantities were drunk there was a moderate diminution in the rate toward the end of the draft, which was not noted in sham-drinking. Dog C drank about twice as fast with the tube as without. It is possible that the sham-drinking of this animal was impeded by the aspiration of air through the upper fistulous opening. Both animals completed their draft of real-drinking within 2 to 4 minutes. That they had correctly removed their deficit was affirmed by their refusal to sham-drink 1 hour later as well as at subsequent periods.

The amount sham-drunk in the last one or two of a series of hourly sham-drinking periods during increasing privation bore a definite relationship to the amount subsequently drunk with the connecting tube. . . . The water deficit of these dogs could thus be computed from the amount of water sham-drunk at hourly periods; dog B sham-drank in one draft approximately 250 per cent of the deficit; dog C sham-drank in 10 minutes 155 per cent to 170 per cent of the deficit. Thus to the three bases of computing water deficit described by Adolph (1939) may be added basis 4 ("sham-drinking deficit").

During the greatest deficit (11 per cent of body weight) developed in dog B, the animal was irritable and the mucous membranes were dry and sticky. The irritability was but briefly allayed by sham-drinking. Following the real-drinking the animal became permanently quiet and relaxed.

Series 2. When sham-drinking was permitted after administration of the estimated water deficit by esophagus, the results varied according to the length of the interval between the completion of administration and the beginning of sham-drinking. The water deficit was computed from the amount sham-drunk in the last series of hourly sham-drinks. From the moment the administration was completed until the end of 9 minutes the dog promptly sham-drank in one draft, *not the amount previously sham-drunk, but only the amount of the deficit.* From the 10th to the 15th minutes inclusively there was an abrupt change in the amount and manner of sham-drinking; the dog sham-drank only small amounts of water or about 20 per cent of the deficit. This sham-drinking was frequently started after a delay and progressed in drafts interspersed with pauses as long as 20 seconds. From the 16th to the 30th minutes inclusively the dog refused to sham-drink. After each of the experiments the dog refused to sham-drink 1 hour later.

This series of experiments, in which water is ingested before it is drunk, reveals the operation of at least two factors in the satisfying of thirst: (1) an immediately acting factor above the fistula, and (2) a factor below the fistula acting after a delay. It further demonstrates that the subfistulous factor has an immediate inhibiting influence on the repetitive act of drinking.

Series 3. Sham-drinking after the intravenous injection of hypertonic solutions varied according to the solution employed. The results were similar in each dog for each solution. Injections required about 1 minute.

During injection of 20 per cent NaCl the dogs began to lick their lips. They started to sham-drink as soon as they were returned to the cage about 1 minute after completion of the injection. The subsequent discontinuous sham-drinking reached its maximal rate 10 minutes after injection, preceding the maximal diuresis by about 15 minutes. It then rapidly declined to a low rate which persisted until the dog was fed at the end of 6 hours. Dog B continued to sham-drink at a low average rate during the night; dog C did not sham-drink after the 6-hour feeding. . . .

Sham-drinking which followed 40 per cent urea differed from that after NaCl in two important respects: (1) it did not begin at once but only after a delay of 10 to 15 minutes; (2) its curve was a miniature replica of that after NaCl. The maximal rate developed within 5 or 10 minutes after sham-drinking started and then subsided within an hour to an average rate one-quarter to one-third that of NaCl for the next 5 hours. The maximal rate was approximately 50 per cent of the maximal rate after NaCl. There was no further sham-drinking after the 6-hour feeding.

Diuresis was also less marked. In dog B maximal diuresis preceded maximal sham-drinking; in dog C maximal diuresis did not occur until 1½ hours later.

The only significant respect in which pitressin affected sham-drinking after NaCl injection was in causing *a delay of 10 to 20 minutes* before sham-drinking started.

Discussion

There are at least two factors concerned in the satisfaction of thirst.

1. Buccal and Pharyngeal Factor. Sham-drinking demonstrates that the passage of water through the mouth and pharynx confers temporary satisfaction of thirst. The amount of water required to do this exceeds but is proportional to the deficit. Several processes are therein concerned. Cannon (1933) and Gregersen (1938) believe satisfaction is secured by wetting the mucous membranes of the mouth and pharynx. Wetting, however, should be as effectively obtained by sham-drinking as by real-drinking, since the rate of drinking is the same in each case. Each gulp of water causes distension of the pharynx before it enters the esophagus. Some human individuals localize their sense of gratification as occurring in the pharynx. The repetitive act of drinking is accomplished by muscular movements of the lips, tongue, pharynx, and respiratory apparatus, which aspirate and propel the water along its course. This repetition of muscular movements is suggested as a possible factor by which satisfaction is secured. Satisfaction is obtained in many instinctive desires by muscular movements. Furthermore, the drinking of fluid constitutes the only condition in which swallowing may be rapidly repeated.

2. The Subpharyngeal Factor. This factor may consist of one or more processes. Entrance of water to the amount of the deficit into the alimentary tract below the pharynx inhibits the repetitive act of drinking to the actual amount of the deficit. This factor also confers permanent satisfaction of thirst after a delay of 10 to 15 minutes. This is shorter than the complete absorption time, for Klisiecki et al. (1933), and others, have determined that the complete absorption of ingested water requires 35 minutes. It is appreciated, however, that the permanency of the satisfaction of this factor may depend on the ultimate absorption of the deficit.

The immediate inhibitory effect of this factor on drinking suggests the operation of mechanical or nervous processes, which might be obtained by the dilatation of parts of the alimentary tube by the water. The permanent but delayed complete satisfaction of thirst may possibly be obtained through the intervention of a pituitary hormone factor.

The sudden appearance of intense thirst during or immediately following the injection of hypertonic NaCl solution is in marked contrast to the gradual development of thirst from water privation. It was the direct result of the addition of NaCl to the body and occurred before the NaCl caused diuresis. Gilman (1937) has suggested that cellular dehydration after NaCl is the stimulus of thirst. While this explanation seems logical for the sustained thirst which occurred later, another factor seems to be concerned in the production of the immediate maximal thirst. Its suppression by pitressin suggests a relationship with the pituitary hypothalamic mechanism, injury of which in diabetes insipidus also causes thirst.

Summary

Dogs with esophageal fistulae were allowed to sham-drink at regular intervals during water privation. The quantities of water sham-drunk were proportional to the water deficit, and provided a basis for computing the deficit. Observations were made on sham-drinking after a quantity of water equal to the deficit had been administered by fistula.

The satisfaction of thirst was found to be not a single process, such as wetting the mucous membranes of the mouth, but a series of at least two supplementary and consecutive processes. Passage of an excessive amount of water through the mouth and pharynx confers immediate but temporary satisfaction of thirst. The repetitive act of drinking and swallowing water is inhibited when the ingested water deficit enters the gut below the upper esophagus. The short period of temporary satisfaction secured by the passage of water through the mouth and pharynx is superseded by the delayed process of permanent satisfaction operating lower in the gut.

Sham-drinking was allowed *ad libitum* after the intravenous injection of hypertonic solutions of NaCl or urea. After NaCl sham-drinking started at once and reached a maximum in 10 minutes, preceding the maximal diuresis. After urea, sham-drinking started after a delay of 10 to 15 minutes. Pitressin administration before NaCl injection inhibited sham-drinking for 10 to 20 minutes.

REFERENCES

Adolph, E. F. Measurements of water drinking in dogs. *Amer. J. Physiol.*, 1939, **125**, 75–86.

Bellows, R. T., and Van Wagenen, W. P. Relationship of polydipsia and polyuria in diabetes insipidus: Study of experimental diabetes insipidus in dogs with and without esophageal fistulae. *J. nerv. ment. Dis.*, 1938, **88**, 417–473.

Birner, M. Eine verbesserte Methode zur Chlorbestimmung Organen und Nahrungsmitteln. *Ztschr. ges. exper. Med.*, 1928, **61**, 700–706.

Cannon, W. B. Some modern extensions of Beaumont's studies on Alexis St. Martin: Thirst and hunger (Beaumont lecture). *J. Mich. Med. Soc.*, 1933, **32**, 155–164.

Darrow, D. C., and Yannett, H. Changes in distribution of body water accompanying increase and decrease in extracellular electrolyte. *J. clin. Invest.*, 1935, **14**, 266–275.

Eisenman, A. J. Note on Van Slyke method for determination of chlorides in blood and tissue. *J. biol. Chem.*, 1929, **82**, 411–414.

Folin, O., and Wu, H. A system of blood analysis. *J. biol. Chem.*, 1919, **38**, 81–110.

Folin, O., and Youngburg, G. E.   The direct determination of urea in urine by direct nesslerization. *J. biol. Chem.*, 1919, **38**, 111–112.

Gilman, A.   Relation between blood osmotic pressure, fluid distribution and voluntary water intake. *Amer. J. Physiol.*, 1937, **120**, 323–328.

Gregersen, M. I.   The distribution and regulation of water in the body. In P. Bard (Ed.), *MacLeod's Physiology in modern medicine*, 8th ed. St. Louis: C. V. Mosby, 1938. Pp. 903–933.

Klisiecki, A., Pickford, M., Rothschild, P., and Verney, E. B.   Absorption and excretion of water by mammal: Relation between absorption of water and its excretion by innervated and denervated kidney. *Proc. Roy. Soc., London, B*, 1933, **112**, 496–521.

Smith, H. W.   Absorption and excretion of water and salts by marine teleosts. *Amer. J. Physiol.*, 1930, **93**, 480–505.

Van Slyke, D. D.   The determination of chlorides in blood and tissues. *J. biol. Chem.*, 1923, **58**, 523–529.

Bellows points out the importance of two factors in the regulation of drinking: (1) the passage of water through the mouth and throat by swallowing, and (2) the absorption of water into the blood via the digestive tract. But which of these is the primary regulator? Or do both factors operate through a single center in the central nervous system? In regard to these questions, Bellows mentions the possible importance of a "pituitary hypothalamic mechanism."

In the following article, Bengt Andersson, a Scandinavian physiologist, attempted to locate a brain area directly involved in the production of thirst. For this purpose, he directed hypertonic NaCl solutions to specific brain areas in goats in order to produce drinking by dehydrating a specific set of cells.

THE EFFECT OF INJECTIONS OF HYPERTONIC NaCl SOLUTIONS INTO DIFFERENT PARTS OF THE HYPOTHALAMUS OF GOATS*

Bengt Andersson

The cause of the intake of water has never been fully understood. Much evidence has been given against the theory of Cannon (1918) that the sensation of thirst is locally generated by dryness of the

* Reprinted from *Acta Physiologica Scandinavica*, Vol. 28, 1953, pp. 188–201. By permission. Copyright © 1953 by *Acta Physiologica Scandinavica*.

mucous membranes of the mouth and throat. Thus the sensation of thirst persists if the nerve supply to the mouth is interrupted (Bellows and Van Wagenen, 1939) and the thirst sensation can be inhibited by giving water by stomach tube.

On the other hand, the experiments of Gilman (1937) show that an elevation of the osmotic pressure of the blood in dogs by intravenous injection of hypertonic solutions of NaCl gives a much greater intake of water than an equivalent rise in osmotic pressure caused by the injection of urea. This indicates that cellular dehydration is the prime factor in arousing thirst. But the fact that primary polydipsia can be caused by a tumor, a cyst (Fulton and Bailey, 1929; Kourilsky, 1950) or experimental injuries (Bailey and Bremer, 1921; Bellows and Van Wagenen, 1938) in the hypothalamus makes it likely that the sensation of thirst generates from this part of the brain. It could thus be postulated that osmoreceptors, situated in the hypothalamus, were involved in the thirst mechanism.

In order to study the effect of an increased osmotic pressure in the hypothalamus, injections of hypertonic NaCl solutions were performed directly into this part of the brain stem of unanaesthetized goats. A polydipsic effect of such injections was recently reported in two short communications (Andersson, 1952a, b). In this paper a full report of the experiments will be given, as well as the results of the histological examinations.

Methods

In all, 19 goats of different age and size were used—some of them for more than one experiment. The operations were performed, with the animals placed in a stand, under local anaesthesia completed with light ether narcosis where the animals reacted to the incision. Hess's (1949) technique was applied for fixation and guidance of the cannulae, the length of which varied according to the size of the skulls and the point of stimulation desired. The cannulae used for the injections were, after having been guided into the hypothalamus, screwed up to a holder that had earlier been fixed on the skull. Injections could thus be performed without displacing the cannulae. These were 0.5 mm. in diameter and the injections were performed through a small hole 0.5–1 mm. (in the earlier experiments 3–6 mm.) from their tip. Thus, the injections could either be rostrally or caudally directed.

Body-warm NaCl solutions of varying concentration were used for the injections, which as a rule were carried out with the animals placed in the same stand as that used for the operations. The animals were offered water from a basin immediately before and after each injection. X-ray pictures of the skull were taken before and during or after each experiment in order to secure and control the position of the cannulae.

When the animals had been killed, the heads were perfused, first with saline and then with 8 per cent formaldehyde solution. In some cases a small amount of Evans blue or India ink was injected through the cannulae before the animal was killed. Most of the brains were embedded in celloidin, cut in serial sections 40–60 microns thick, stained with toluidin blue and histologically examined. In this way the localization of most points of injection could be determined. . . .

Results

The abbreviated protocols of two experiments are given below, one in which a very large effect was obtained, and another with a negative result.

May 5, 1952. Goat no. 16. Weight about 35 kg.

11:40–12:20. Operation. The cannula was placed on the caudal part of the holder. Two injections of 0.1 cc. of 2 per cent NaCl solution were not followed by any drinking

Localization: The point of injection was situated caudally in the third ventricle in the dorsal hypothalamic region.

13:25. A new cannula was placed on the rostral part of the holder.

13:50. Injection of 0.15 cc. of 2 per cent NaCl solution. Half a minute after the injection the animal drank very greedily 3.1 liters of water. It had refused to drink immediately before the injection.

13:55. Urine. Amount: 50 cc. Sp. gr. 1.035. 20 minutes later the animal was again offered water, and now it drank in three stages, some minutes between each, 6.1 liters of water.

14:40. Renewed injection as at 13:50 did not induce any further drinking.

14:47. Urine. Amount: 50 cc. Sp. gr. 1.034.

15:03. Renewed injection without effect.

15:21. Urine. Amount: 33 cc. Sp. gr. 1.033.

16:05. Urine. Amount: 150 cc. Sp. gr. 1.008.

16:30. Urine. Amount: 155 cc. Sp. gr. 1.003. Between 16:30 and 17:10 was collected 490 cc. of urine with a specific gravity of 1.002. The course of the polyuria was not followed overnight. The animal was killed the next morning.

Localization: The point of injection was situated in the middle hypo-thalamic region rostral and somewhat medial to Columna fornix de-scendens on the left side. The injection was performed in caudal direction and was not seen to have broken through the ventricular wall.

August 29, 1952. Animal no. 19.

10:40–11:05. Operation. Three consecutive injections of 0.05–0.1 cc. of 2 per cent NaCl solution induced no drinking, but visibly irritated the animal. The experiment lasted for 2 hours. Just before it ended the animal urinated. Amount: 70 cc. Sp. gr. 1.009.

Localization: The point of injection was situated on the right side in the region of the optic chiasm. Injection in caudal direction.

The points where injection of hypertonic NaCl solution had a polydipsic effect were all situated medially in the hypothalamus in the vicinity of the third ventricle.

The most obvious effect was obtained in five experiments; in three of them, the points of injection were near to Columna fornix de-scendens at a horizontal section approximately through the middle of the hypothalamus. Here the injected solution was not seen to have broken through the ventricular wall.

In six out of seven experiments, where the injections were made into the third ventricle or where the injected solution visibly had broken through the ventricular wall, the injections were followed by water drinking of the animals. However, the polydipsic effect in these cases seemed to be less pronounced, but was more easily re-peatable after renewed injections.

In three experiments injection of 0.8–0.9 per cent NaCl solution caused no drinking, but subsequent injections of 2 per cent NaCl solution were effective in this respect.

Injections in the lateral part of the hypothalamus and in the vicinity of the optic chiasm did not induce any water drinking, possibly with the exception of one experiment, where injection of strongly hyper-tonic solution in the rostral part of the median eminence on one occasion was followed by drinking of the animal. Two to four hours after the experiment started, an obviously increased urine secretion together with diminished concentration of the urine was observed in seven cases. In at least one of them this polyuria was not the conse-quence of an increased intake of water.

In six experiments no increased diuresis was observed, but here the observation of the animals lasted only for 2–3½ hours.

To three of the animals water was administered by stomach tube. In two of these experiments the injection of hypertonic NaCl solution did not cause any visible change in the subsequent water diuresis. Here the injected salt solution had visibly emerged into the third ventricle and previous injections of the same kind had induced water drinking. In the third experiment, where the point of injection was in the rostral part of the median eminence, injections of 0.1 cc. of 4 per cent NaCl solution were followed by decreased urine flow and a marked concentration of the urine. Any polydipsic effect at this point of injection was very doubtful.

Discussion

The important role played by hypothalamic centres in the regulation of water metabolism has been elucidated in several ways. Thus Fisher, Ingram, and Ranson (1938) demonstrated that the supraoptic nuclei are directly involved in the antidiuretic function of the neurohypophysis, and it has been shown (Bailey and Bremer, 1921; Bellows and Van Wagenen, 1938) that injuries to the ventral part of the hypothalamus, without direct damage to the posterior pituitary, can lead to temporary and permanent diabetes insipidus. Investigations, especially those of Verney (1947), have also demonstrated the presence of osmotically sensitive cells within the part of the brain which is supplied by the internal carotid arteries. The possible localization of such cells to the supraoptic and paraventricular nuclei has been postulated. It has also been shown that dehydration as well as overloading of the antidiuretic function by injection of hypertonic sodium chloride solutions in rats leads to a chromatolytic reaction in the nerve cells of both the supraoptic and the magno-cellular portions of the paraventricular nuclei (Hillarp, 1949). However, the question of whether the paraventricular nuclei are involved in the regulation of the function of the posterior pituitary is not settled, as Harris (1947) showed that electrical stimulation of the supraoptic nuclei caused secretion of antidiuretic hormone from the neurohypophysis, but stimulation of the paraventricular nuclei in the same way did not have this effect.

The role played by the hypothalamus in the regulation of the water intake is more obscure. The strong increase of the intake of water seen soon after section of the pituitary stalk and often after other lesions in the hypothalamus seems to be secondary to a preceding polyuria (Richter, 1935; Fisher, Magoun, and Hetherington, 1938; Fisher, Ingram, and Ranson 1938). On the other hand, the polydipsia in some cases of diabetes insipidus (Fulton and Bailey, 1929; Kourilsky, 1950) or sometimes after experimental hypothalamic injury (Bailey and Bremer, 1921; Bellows and Van Wagenen,

1938) is not always preceded by a polyuria. These findings would indicate that some hypothalamic structure also is involved in the regulation of water intake. If this structure, however, were identical to the supraoptic nuclei or closely associated with them, the destruction of this region of the hypothalamus would inhibit the normal water intake and produce a state of dehydration. But this seems not to be the case, as Fisher, Ingram, and Ranson (1938) showed that the polyuria seen after a severe damage to the supraoptic region was followed by an obvious polydipsia.

On the other hand, rats with bilateral lesions in the ventromedian region of the hypothalamus develop a chronic state of relative dehydration, and this is suggested to be the result of a destruction of neural elements governing the water intake (Stevenson, Welt, and Orloff, 1950). An experimental support for the eliciting of thirst feelings from this part of the hypothalamus was also given by Brügger (1943), who compiled the results of electrical stimulation in the hypothalamus, earlier obtained by W. R. Hess. He found that hyperphagia was often combined with increased thirst when stimulating within a region near to the ventricular wall in the middle part of the hypothalamus, and considered that this would indicate that the urge to eat and drink are elicited from hypothalamic regions adjacent to each other.

The experiments here described were designed to observe whether a local rise in the osmotic pressure by injection of hypertonic sodium chloride solution into some part of the hypothalamus could produce a sensation of thirst. This seems to have been the case within a region medially in the hypothalamus near to the third ventricle, while injections into the supraoptic region or laterally in the hypothalamus did not seem to have this effect. From these experiments, however, it is not possible to determine from which structure in the medial hypothalamus the effect was elicited, as very little is known about the spread of the injected solutions. Neither do the experiments give any real proof for the existence of cells within this region, reacting specifically to osmotic stimulation, as hypertonic NaCl solutions of the concentration used probably have a general stimulating effect on nerve cells.

That the simple mechanical effect of the injections could be of any importance is unlikely, as injections of iso- and hypotonic solutions did not cause any drinking.

Since in most cases injections into the third ventricle were followed by water drinking, it further seems as if the tissue from which the thirst was elicited was situated near the ventricular wall. The thirst stimulation caused by injections into the ventricle was, however, as judged from the amount of water drunk, not as strong as in some other experiments, where the injected solution did not seem to have emerged into the ventricle. Intraventricular injections, on the other hand, probably caused less damage to the tissue reacting to the stimulus, as the effect here was more easily repeatable.

The experiments thus show that nervous tissue involved in the regulation of the water intake is situated in the hypothalamus somewhere in the vicinity of the third ventricle, and might be taken as a support for the assumption that this tissue consists of cells reacting specifically to a rise in the extracellular osmotic pressure. This could explain why in most cases of diabetes insipidus and of experimental injuries to the hypothalamus the polyuria precedes the polydipsia, though in certain cases quite the contrary is seen. Severe damage to the supraoptic region might leave most of the mechanism eliciting thirst intact. Thus a polydipsia should be seen as a consequence to the polyuria. On the other hand, an injury irritating structures involved in the thirst mechanism, without a simultaneous inactivation of the supraoptico-hypophysial system, could cause a primary polydipsia.

As yet, however, the effect of other hypertonic solutions than sodium chloride has not been tried. This would be of interest, as recent work has shown that the non-electrolyte sorbitol and sucrose, when injected intravenously, are as effective as NaCl in producing drinking, whereas glucose (Holmes and Gregersen, 1950) and urea (Gilman, 1937) are much less effective in this respect. Verney (1947) has shown that the stimulating effect of these substances on the osmoreceptors regulating the secretion of antidiuretic hormone is of the same order.

The strongest thirst stimulus from one single intrahypothalamic injection of hypertonic NaCl solution was obtained in experiment no. 4, where the animal drank more than 9 liters of water. As could be seen from the histological examination, the injected salt solution had not caused any damage to the ventricular wall, although some of the injected solution might have diffused into the ventricle. The point of injection was here situated in the middle hypothalamic region rostral to the paraventricular nucleus on the left side and the injection was directed caudally. In this case it seems likely that cells within the paraventricular nucleus or close to it have reacted to the osmotic stimulus and elicited the sensation of thirst. The increased activity of cells within this nucleus seen after dehydration (Hillarp, 1949) supports this assumption.

The fact that the animal did not drink the whole amount of water at once could either have been due to a temporary inhibition of the thirst from the alimentary tract when a certain amount of water had been drunk, or it may have depended on a gradual spread of the solution to more and more of the sensitive tissue, or it may have been the combined result of both. In this experiment, two new injections about an hour after the first had no effect. It is possible that the stimulus was not sufficient any more to elicit further drinking since the animal had overloaded itself with water after the first injection. Another possibility is that the first injection had first stimulated but then inactivated the sensitive tissue.

This experiment also most obviously shows that an extreme polydipsia can precede a polyuria after hypothalamic stimulation, as earlier shown to be the case sometimes after hypothalamic injuries (Bailey and Bremer, 1921; Bellows and Van Wagenen, 1938).

The increased diuresis seen in these experiments have, however, not always been preceded by a polydipsia, and it seems very possible that a polyuria would have occurred in some of the experiments even if the animals had not been offered water after the injections. The onset (2–4 hours after the hypothalamic incision) and the course of this polyuria very much resembles that seen in the temporary phase of experimental diabetes insipidus (Bellows and Van Wagenen, 1938).

Only three experiments were performed, where intrahypothalamic injections of hypertonic sodium chloride solution were made into previously hydrated animals, and of these hardly any conclusions can be drawn. In the single experiment where an inhibition of the water diuresis was seen as a consequence to the injections, the point of injection was situated in the rostral part of the median eminence. A spread of the injected solution to the supraoptic region is possible; but, as in this case strongly hypertonic NaCl solution (4 per cent) was used, it is just as likely that the supraoptico-hypophysial tract was directly stimulated. A stimulation of the posterior pituitary as a consequence to the fixation of the cannula in its position must also be suspected here, as the water diuresis did not appear until 4½ hours after the animal had been strongly hydrated.

Summary

In goats, intrahypothalamic injections of hypertonic NaCl solutions, within a region medially in the vicinity of the third ventricle, induced drinking of the animals. The most obvious effect was obtained in experiments where the injection was performed in the middle hypothalamic region near the paraventricular nucleus.

Injections of iso- or hypotonic solutions did not have this effect. Injections of hypertonic NaCl solution in the lateral parts of the hypothalamus and in the vicinity of the optic chiasm did not induce any drinking.

In seven experiments, an obviously increased diuresis together with a diminished concentration of the urine was observed 2–4 hours after the experiments had started. This polyuria was not in every case the consequence of an increased intake of water.

REFERENCES

Andersson, B. Polydipsia caused by intrahypothalamic injections of hypertonic NaCl-solutions. *Experientia*, 1952, **8** (4), 157–158. (a)

Andersson, B. Polydipsia following injections of hypertonic sodium chloride solution into hypothalamus. *Nord. Med.*, 1952, **47**, 663–664. (b)

Bailey, P., and Bremer, F. Experimental diabetes insipidus. *Arch. int. Med.*, 1921, **28**, 773–803.

Bellows, R. T., and Van Wagenen, W. P. Relationship of polydipsia and polyuria in diabetes insipidus: Study of experimental diabetes insipidus in dogs with and without esophageal fistulae. *J. nerv. ment. Dis.*, 1938, **88**, 417–473.

Bellows, R. T., and Van Wagenen, W. P. Effect of resection of olfactory, gustatory and trigeminal nerves on water drinking in dogs without and with diabetes insipidus. *Amer. J. Physiol.*, 1939, **126**, 13–19.

Brügger, M. Fresstrieb als hypothalamisches Symptom. *Helvet. Physiol. Pharmacol. Acta*, 1943, **1**, 183–198.

Cannon, W. B. The physiological basis of thirst. *Proc. Roy. Soc., London, B*, 1918, **90**, 283–301.

Fisher, C., Ingram, W. R., and Ranson, S. W. Diabetes insipidus and the neuro-hormonal control of water balance. Ann Arbor, Mich.: Edwards Bros., 1938.

Fisher, C., Magoun, H. W., and Hetherington, A. Effect of water deprivation on fluid exchange of cats with diabetes insipidus. *Amer. J. Physiol.*, 1938, **121**, 112–122.

Fulton, J. F., and Bailey, P. Tumors in region of third ventricle: Their diagnosis and relation to pathological sleep. *J. nerv. ment. Dis.*, 1929, **69**, 1, 145, 261.

Gilman, A. Relation between blood osmotic pressure, fluid distribution and voluntary water intake. *Amer. J. Physiol.*, 1937, **120**, 323–328.

Harris, G. W. The innervation and actions of the neurohypophysis: An investigation using the method of remote-control stimulation. *Phil. Trans. Roy. Soc., London, B*, 1947, **232**, 385–441.

Hess, W. R. *Das Zwischenhirn*. Basel: Schwabe, 1949.

Hillarp, N. A. Cell reactions in hypothalamus following overloading of antidiuretic function. *Acta Endocrinol.*, 1949, **2**, 33–43.

Holmes, J. H., and Gregersen, M. I. Observations on drinking induced by hypertonic solutions. *Amer. J. Physiol.*, 1950, **162**, 326–337.

Kourilsky, R.   Discussion: The diagnosis of diabetes insipidus. *Proc. Roy. Soc. Med.*, 1950, **43**, 842–843.

Richter, C. P.   Primacy of polyuria in diabetes insipidus. *Amer. J. Physiol.*, 1935, **112**, 481–487.

Stevenson, J. A. F., Welt, L. G., and Orloff, S.   Abnormalities of water and electrolyte metabolism in rats with hypothalamic lesions. *Amer. J. Physiol.*, 1950, **161**, 35–39.

Verney, E. B.   Antidiuretic hormone and factors which determine its release. *Proc. Roy. Soc., London, B*, 1947, **135**, 25–106.

Andersson's research located a possible "thirst center" within the hypothalamus. Is thirst produced by this center alone, or must other areas also be involved? Is this center involved only in thirst, or is it important also in the operation of other motives, such as hunger? For studying the function of brain areas, two main methods have generally been used: (1) Ablation, or removal of the brain area under study. If, as a result of ablation, experimental animals lose the behavior being studied, whereas the control animals retain that behavior, we may conclude that the area removed is necessary for the behavior observed, though it may not be sufficient—that is, other areas may also be necessary. (2) Electrical or chemical stimulation of the area. If, when stimulated in the "thirst center," an animal begins to drink, as in Andersson's study, its behavior supports the idea that the particular area is involved in producing thirst.

The following study, by psychologist S. P. Grossman, uses a new stimulation technique involving chemicals in solid rather than liquid form to control the spread of the chemical effect. The effect produced by this technique depends on the particular chemical used, and indicates that a single brain area may underlie more than one type of motivated behavior.

EATING OR DRINKING ELICITED BY DIRECT ADRENERGIC OR CHOLINERGIC STIMULATION OF THE HYPOTHALAMUS*

S. P. Grossman

The exploration of the central nervous system by means of electrical stimulation has provided a wealth of information of great in-

* Reprinted from *Science,* Vol. 132, July 29, 1960, pp. 301–302. By permission. Copyright © 1960 by the American Association for the Advancement of Science.

terest to physiologists and psychologists alike. The usefulness of this technique is limited, however, because the effects of stimulation are not restricted to synaptic junctions, but affect fibers of passage, causing conduction in both normal and antidromic directions.

It has long been recognized that chemical stimulation avoids these problems, but the technique has in the past been plagued by the problem of uncontrolled spread, which raises a serious objection to the injection of chemicals in solution. Attempts to control for this factor by minimizing the injected quantities have apparently not been completely successful in preventing the escape of the fluid along the shank of the needle, following the path of least resistance.

Depositing chemicals in solid form has been shown to reduce this problem greatly (MacLean, 1957); but this method has not allowed repeated stimulation of a selected locus. In the present study, a technique was developed which avoids this objection.

Method

A double cannula system, consisting of two modified syringe needles, was permanently implanted unilaterally, by means of a stereotaxic instrument, into the lateral hypothalamus of each of 12 albino rates. Histological verification of the intended placements showed the tip of the cannula to be located in a circumscribed perifornical region at the same rostrocaudal coordinate as the ventromedial nucleus, an area corresponding to the ventral portion of Anand and Brobeck's "feeding area" of the lateral hypothalamus (Anand and Brobeck, 1951).

After 5 days of postoperative recuperation, the inner cannula was removed and minute amounts (1 to 5 micrograms) of crystalline chemicals were tapped into its tip before it was returned to its usual position. Successive treatments were administered to all animals in a counterbalanced order, with a minimum of 3 days between injections. Both food and water were freely available throughout the experiment. The food and water consumption of satiated rats was recorded for 1 hour immediately following stimulation and compared with the consumption in a comparable period immediately preceding the injection. Daily food and water consumption records were maintained.

Results

None of the animals ever consumed food or water in measurable quantities during the prestimulation period. The injection of epinephrine or norepinephrine resulted in highly significant ($p < .01$) food consumption beginning 5 to 10 minutes after stimulation and persisting with variable intensity for 20 to 40 minutes. Food consumption averaged 3.0 gm. under epinephrine and 4.3 gm. under norepinephrine.

The injection of acetylcholine (capped by physostigmine) or carbachol into the identical loci in the same animals resulted in highly significant drinking ($p < .01$), the latency, duration, and magnitude of the effect being comparable to those obtained for eating after the injection of adrenergic substances. Water consumption averaged 7.4 milliliters after the injection of acetylcholine and 12.8 milliliters after the injection of carbachol, this difference being highly significant ($p < .01$). There was no significant food consumption after cholinergic stimulation (see Fig. 1).

The injection of adrenergic substances resulted in significantly less water intake than did cholinergic stimulation ($p < .01$). Since in all

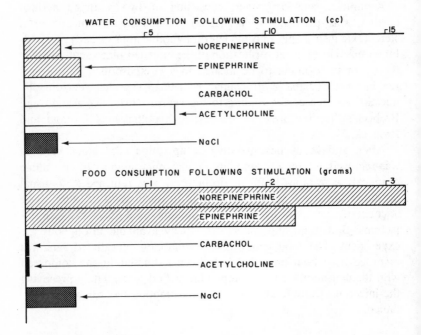

Figure 1. *Food and water intake during 1 hour following stimulation. (The intake during a comparable control period was zero in all cases and is not shown.)*

but one animal the drinking occurred only after a considerable amount of dry food had been consumed, water consumption seemed to be secondary to the food intake rather than a direct consequence of stimulation. To establish further the specificity of the adrenergic effect, norepinephrine was deposited in the lateral hypothalamus of six food- and water-satiated animals, which were then placed in observation cages containing only water. For 30 minutes after the injection none of the animals consumed measurable quantities of water, though four of them repeatedly sampled the drinking tube very briefly. Food was then introduced, and all animals ate almost immediately, though total food consumption was lower than that normally observed, since the food was introduced only toward the end of the period previously established as the duration of the adrenergic effect.

In order to control for the effect of osmotic stimulation, comparable amounts of NaCl were deposited in all the animals. No significant food or water intake was observed. In order to control for general excitation effects, strychnine in comparable quantities was deposited in six animals which also showed the above-described effects of adrenergic and cholinergic stimulation. No consummatory behavior was observed following this stimulation.

Discussion

The daily consumption records indicate that the amount of food or water consumed during the 1-hour period after stimulation, totaling as much as 40 per cent of the animal's normal daily intake, appeared to be consumed above and beyond the normal daily intake. Because of the variability of these records, no statistical evaluation of this effect can be presented, but the conclusion is supported, at least for eating, by the consistent weight gain observed on the day following adrenergic stimulation.

A control for the specificity of the localization of the observed effects was obtained in a preliminary study designed to yield optimal stereotaxic coordinates for the study reported here. It was found that very small deviations from the optimal position sufficed to eliminate the effects completely.

The results of this investigation indicate that (1) cell concentrations active in the regulation of both food and water intake are present in the lateral hypothalamus; (2) cell concentrations exerting this control appear to be highly localized but not clearly separate from each other, since stimulation of "identical" loci in the same animal can evoke both forms of behavior; and (3) the feeding mechanism appears to be selectively activated by adrenergic stimulation, while the drinking mechanisms appear to respond selectively to cholinergic stimulation.

Summary

A double cannula system, allowing repeated stimulation of central structures with crystalline chemicals, was developed. This technique was employed to study the effects of adrenergic and cholinergic stimulation of the lateral hypothalamus of rats. Drug-specific effects on the feeding and drinking mechanisms, respectively, were observed.

REFERENCES

Anand, B. K., and Brobeck, J. R.   Localization of "feeding center" in hypothalamus of rat.   *Proc. Soc. exp. Biol. Med.,* 1951, **77,** 323–324.
MacLean, P. D.   Chemical and electrical stimulation of hippocampus in unrestrained animals: I. Methods and electroencephalographic findings. *Arch. Neurol. Psychiat.,* 1957, **78,** 113–127.

Grossman was able to elicit both eating and drinking by stimulating a single brain area with different chemical stimuli. Drinking (i.e., thirst) was produced by stimulation with cholinergic agents; eating (i.e., hunger), by adrenergic agents. No consumption was elicited by direct stimulation with NaCl (control for osmotic effects) or strychnine (control for general excitation effects). Thus thirst appears to be regulated as a cholinergic mechanism involving subcortical areas of the brain, particularly in the hypothalamus. (For more complete accounts of Grossman's work in this area, see S. P. Grossman, Direct adrenergic and cholinergic stimulation of hypothalamic mechanisms, Amer. J. Physiol., 1962, 202, 872–882; and Effects of adrenergic and cholinergic blocking agents on hypothalamic mechanisms, Amer. J. Physiol., 1962, 202, 1230–1236).

What areas comprise the total mechanism that is both necessary and sufficient for the production of thirst? In the following article, psychologists Alan E. Fisher and John N. Coury discuss their use of cholinergic stimulants in an attempt to trace the nerve circuitry for thirst.

CHOLINERGIC TRACING OF A CENTRAL NEURAL CIRCUIT UNDERLYING THE THIRST DRIVE*

Alan E. Fisher and John N. Coury

Recent work with chemical stimulation of the brain (Grossman, 1960; Morgane, 1961a, b) has correlated application of cholinergic drugs to the perifornical region with drinking behavior, and application of adrenergic drugs to the perifornical and far lateral hypothalamic areas with eating. The data suggest that the thirst drive is partly regulated by cholinergic action, and the hunger drive, by adrenergic action.

In early investigations in this area we were concerned with the possible central action of insulin or glucagon, or both, on brain systems related to hunger and satiety. No evidence for such action was uncovered, and early work with adrenergic drugs proved inconclusive.

A series of experiments with cholinergic drugs, however, is providing evidence that the perifornical region is only one of many brain areas in which localized application of minute quantities of cholinergic agents is followed by a marked increase in drinking.

Method

The basic experimental procedures are as follows. Adult albino or hooded rats are prepared for experimentation by stereotaxic implantation of hypodermic guide shafts. The animals are then returned to special cages that contain feeding and drinking receptacles designed to permit continual and accurate measurement of food and water intake. The water dispenser consists of the graduated section of a 50-cc. buret and a detachable Plexiglas drinking well. The well is set in a plastic block to prevent spilling, and direct readings from the buret can be made during the test. On testing days, a 30-gauge cannula containing pure crystals or a chemical in solution is set in an implant connector and lowered to the target area. The technique permits introduction of 1 to 3 micrograms of crystalline substance or as little as 0.0001 cc. of solution per injection. Response to a series of placebos and experimental drugs is tested and retested at each brain site, each

* Reprinted from *Science*, Vol. 138, 1962, pp. 691–693. By permission. Copyright © 1962 by the American Association for the Advancement of Science.

test being separated from the next by at least 24 hours. Food and water are continuously available to the animals, and the data recorded include measures of food and water intake for the pretest and the test hour, as well as daily 24-hour readings.

Results

Thus far, 94 male adult rats have been permanently cannulated in a wide sampling of brain areas. Each rat has been given an extended series of brain injection tests which include at least four separate tests with carbachol. Table 1 gives the major positive brain areas thus far located in replicate testing, as well as the average amounts of water consumed, during the hour following cholinergic stimulation, by animals whose response was positive. Control measures obtained during pretest hours, and after injection of placebos and noncholinergic drugs, have been consistently and significantly below these levels. The mean hourly drinking response during pretest hours in animals whose response to cholinergic stimulation was positive was 1.4 cc., and the mean drinking response in the hour following injection of placebos or noncholinergic test chemicals was 1.2 cc. Brain areas which, to

Table 1. *Brain areas for which results were positive (that is, injected carbachol induced drinking).*

Positive brain structures	Animals (N)	Water intake (cm.^{3}) *	
		Mean (4–8 tests/N)	Maximum
Dorsomedial hippocampus—area of dentate gyrus†	6	20.7	56
Septal regions†	6	14.0	31
Area of diagonal band†	3	17.5	40
Reuniens-mesial thalamic†	5	13.7	45
Perifornical	5	9.7	16
Preoptic regions	5	10.0	19
Lateral hypothalamic—medial forebrain bundle	6	8.5	17
Mammillary-interpeduncular regions	4	10.2	17
Anterior nuclei of thalamus (anterodorsal, anteroventral)	5	8.9	15
Cingulate cortex	3	12.5	22

* During the hour following cholinergic stimulation.
† Water intake above 20 cc. was frequently recorded.

date, have yielded negative results (mean water intake of less than 4 cc.; maximum intake of less than 8 cc.) are as follows: posterior hippocampus, lateral hippocampus, midbrain tegmentum, amygdaloid areas, lateral thalamic areas, ventromedial area of the hypothalamus, paraventricular nucleus of the thalamus, frontal cortex, subiculum, entorhinal areas, piriform cortex, and most or all of the caudate nucleus (results were positive in one animal).

In the animals whose response was positive, drinking began 3 to 12 minutes after insertion of the carbachol-plugged cannula into the site and continued intermittently for 20 to 40 minutes in most cases. The longest periods of drinking response were recorded for animals with hippocampal placements. The precise time distribution of the drinking response after injection was not recorded in early stages of the study; additional tests are being made, with other animals, to determine whether onset and duration of drinking vary consistently with placement.

All animals tested had a single brain implant and could be stimulated only in a single vertical plane. The cannula containing the crystalline chemical plug could be inserted to several successive depths but was never lowered beyond the point where a positive response was first obtained in the individual animal.

After a series of control and experimental tests the animals were sacrificed and the brains were sectioned and stained. The end of the track left by the implant guide shaft, or by the internal cannula if it was lower, was considered to be the stimulation site.

Discussion

Several points of theoretical interest should be particularly noted. First, all of the positive areas for drinking thus far found lie within the positive reinforcement system traced by Olds and others in rats in self-stimulation experiments. [See the report by Olds in the section on Electrical Self-Stimulation of the Brain—Ed.] Second, the data may become even more meaningful when related to a circuit postulated and outlined by Papez (1937). Papez suggested that a series of structures, principally including the hippocampus, the fornix, the mammillary regions of the hypothalamus, the mammillothalamic tract, the anterior nuclei of the thalamus, the cingulate gyrus, and again the hippocampus, composed an interconnected, functional circuit related to the expression of emotion in man and animals. Most of the brain areas found by us to be positive for the drinking response are either part of the original Papez circuit or closely integrated with it.

Our findings suggest that the controlling units involve the dentate gyrus and the H_1 pyramidal cell fields of the medial-dorsal hippocampus (Green, 1960), which project principally to the mammillary regions by way of the dorsal fornix. Nauta has stated that fibers from the dorsal hippocampus of the rat also project to the septal regions, the nucleus of the diagonal band, the preoptic regions, and the anterior and midline nuclei of the thalamus. Other studies confirm his statement for many of these projections. Midline thalamic nuclei, in turn, project to the cingulate gyrus, and there is some evidence for an interconnection between lateral preoptic, lateral hypothalamic, and septal region, the septal region providing a rich two-way circuit with the dorsal hippocampus and presumably with the H_1 pyramidal fields by way of the dentate gyrus (Daitz and Powell, 1954; Green, 1960; Guillery, 1956; Jasper, 1960; Nauta, 1956; Powell and Cowan, 1955).

It is thus feasible to include all major positive areas within a medially oriented, generalized Papez circuit, although it is perhaps equally relevant at this stage to postulate a more complex interaction between medial forebrain bundle and fornix system. The preoptic regions could be much more clearly implicated through involvement of the medial forebrain bundle, and we have preliminary but unreplicated evidence that the medial parolfactory area, a contributor to the medial forebrain bundle, may be a positive area. The overall data thus provide close correlation with findings reported in MacLean and Ploog's recent paper (1962) concerned with the identification of primate brain areas in which electrical stimulation was correlated with penile erection, and in Robinson and Mishkin's report (1962) relative to food and water ingestion after electrical stimulation of the primate brain. Many of the areas implicated in the three separate studies are the same, and the evidence appears strong that circuits mediating each of the primary drives will be found to follow generally parallel courses through the limbic system and diencephalon. Specific chemical keys or stimulation techniques may be necessary to isolate and trace separate functional circuits, but such tools seem to be rapidly becoming available (Fisher, 1956, 1961; Grossman, 1960; MacLean and Ploog, 1962; Morgane, 1961a, b; Robinson and Mishkin, 1962).

In this connection, our recent emphasis has been on testing animals under conditions which maximize the possibility of measuring changes related to any primary drive during chemical stimulation of the brain. One animal has been found that consistently responds to injection of carbachol by drinking, to injection of noradrenalin by eating, and to injection of a soluble steroid by building nests. All three chemicals have been applied to the same rhinencephalic locus at the junction of the area of the diagonal band of Broca and the medial preoptic region, and all three effects are specific with respect to the chemical or chemical family implicated.

Another aspect of the data worth discussing is the finding that some of the positive areas produce a significantly greater drinking response than others (see Table 1). The density of selectively sensitive neurons in an area, or the precision of delivery to a positive locus, may be involved, but other possibilities suggest themselves. All but one of the positive areas (reuniens) for which an attendant water intake of 20 cc. or more is frequently recorded are in the hippocampus or directly project to it. It is thus possible that sustained hippocampal after discharge is responsible for the prolonged and accentuated drinking that follows cholinergic stimulation of these areas. Electroencephalographic recording should reveal any correlations between separate types of hippocampal electrical activity and drinking. A second, but currently less likely, hypothesis is that the hippocampus normally functions as an inhibitory part of the drive system and that carbachol produces local seizures which temporarily disrupt hippocampal function and indirectly increase drive. Again, it should be possible to select between hypotheses by utilizing electroencephalographic techniques with animals prepared with multiple combinations of chemical and electrical implants.

Finally, it should be stated that the correlation between drinking and cholinergic stimulation of the brain is remarkably specific. It is true that we have found five cases in which injection of carbachol increased both eating and drinking, and one in which injection of either carbachol or strychnine consistently led to marked increases in food and water intake, but such cases or loci are quite rare. Animals injected with carbachol in the designated brain areas show a highly selective water-ingestion response and typically ignore stimuli allied to other primary drives for at least 20 to 30 minutes after drug injection. Such facts appear to weigh against the possibility that random firing or seizure activity in the limbic system underlies the response and that no true circuit is being traced. Indiscriminate neural firing would be expected to disrupt integrated response, or to influence a number of drives, rather than to selectively increase drinking.

In summary, the data of this study seem of particular interest because of the implication that a functional neural circuit can be traced through a selective sensitivity to a chemical agent, or to a particular range of concentration of that agent. Our own research (Fisher, 1956, 1961) and that of others (Grossman, 1960; Morgane, 1961a,

b) has previously implicated only single or isolated loci, with little indication that entire circuits or their synaptic interconnections might be biochemically distinct. In addition, the new evidence, coupled with other recent data from studies of chemical and electrical stimulation of the brain, suggests the probability that relatively parallel neural circuits coursing through the limbic system and associated brain areas underlie the mediation of the primary drives.

Summary

Cholinergic stimulation of any of a number of interrelated limbic and diencephalic structures in the rat elicits a rapid and marked increase in water intake. We postulate that a generalized Papez circuit mediates the thirst drive, that the circuit is specifically and functionally sensitive to cholinergic action, and that other primary drives depend on closely parallel neural circuits partitioned both structurally and biochemically.

REFERENCES

Daitz, H. M., and Powell, T. P. S.   Studies of the connexions of the fornix system.   *J. Neurol. Neurosurg. Psychiat.,* 1954, **17,** 75–82.

Fisher, A. E.   Maternal and sexual behavior induced by intracranial chemical stimulation.   *Science,* 1956, **124,** 228–229.

Fisher, A. E.   Behavior as a function of certain neurobiochemical events. In R. Patton et al., *Current trends in psychological theory.*   Pittsburgh: Univ. of Pittsburgh Press, 1961. Pp. 70–86.

Green, J. D.   The hippocampus.   In J. Field (Ed.), *Handbook of physiology,* Sect. 1, Vol. 2.   Washington, D.C.: American Physiological Soc., 1960. Pp. 1373–1389.

Grossman, S. P.   Eating or drinking elicited by direct adrenergic or cholinergic stimulation of hypothalamus.   *Science,* 1960, **132,** 301–302.

Guillery, R. W.   Degeneration in the post-commissural fornix and the mammillary peduncle of the rat.   *J. Anat.,* 1956, **90,** 350–370.

Jasper, H. H.   Unspecific thalamocortical relations.   In J. Field (Ed.), *Handbook of physiology,* Sect. 1, Vol. 2.   Washington, D.C.: American Physiological Soc., 1960. Pp. 1307–1321.

MacLean, P. D., and Ploog, D. W.   Cerebral representation of penile erection.   *J. Neurophysiol.,* 1962, **25,** 29–55.

Morgane, P. J.   Distinct feeding and hunger motivating systems in the lateral hypothalamus of the rat.   *Science,* 1961, **133,** 887–888.   (a)

Morgane, P. J.   Medial forebrain bundle and "feeding centers" of the hypothalamus.   *J. comp. Neurol.,* 1961, **117,** 1–25.   (b)

Nauta, W. J. H.   An experimental study of the fornix system in the rat. *J. comp. Neurol.,* 1956, **104,** 247–271.

Papez, J. W.   Proposed mechanism of emotion.   *Arch. Neurol. Psychiat.,* 1937, **38,** 725–743.

Powell, T. P. S., and Cowan, W. M.   An experimental study of the efferent connexions of the hippocampus.   *Brain,* 1955, **78,** 115–132.

Robinson, B. W., and Mishkin, M.   Alimentary responses evoked from forebrain structures in macaca mulatta.   *Science,* 1962, **136,** 260–262.

SUGGESTIONS FOR
ADVANCED READING

Falk, John L.   The behavioral regulation of water-electrolyte balance. In M. R. Jones (Ed.), *Nebraska symposium on motivation,* vol. 9. Lincoln: Univ. of Nebraska Press, 1961. Pp. 1–33.

Thirst: Proceedings of the 1st international symposium on thirst in the regulation of body water.   New York: Pergamon, 1964.

Wolf, A. V.   *Thirst.*   Springfield, Ill.: Chas. C Thomas, 1958.

2

MECHANISMS OF
MEMORY

One of the most interesting and persistent problems in physiological psychology is that of memory. Three aspects of this general problem may be considered: (1) Where are memories stored? (2) What are the *substrates,* or material bases, for memories? (3) How are memories recalled? We will discuss each question briefly before presenting the studies.

Where are memories stored? The phrenologists of the nineteenth century supposedly found specific locations not only for memory but for all human faculties, and attempted to analyze human personality in terms of specific bumps on the skull. This attempt was singularly unsuccessful, but the hypothesis of localized memories continued to receive well-planned study. Both Ivan Pavlov and John B. Watson assumed that learning consists of conditioned reflexes that are formed in specific locations in the brain. Against this background worked Karl S. Lashley, the leading physiological psychologist of the early twentieth century. Lashley's prime area of concern was the localization of memory function in the cerebral cortex. He devoted a considerable portion of his scientific career to this question. His findings, and those of his colleagues, have pointed away from anatomical localization of specific memories. In reviewing his thirty years of research "in search of the engram," Lashley summarized: "This series of experiments has yielded a good bit of information about what and where the memory trace is not. It has discovered nothing directly of the real nature of the engram. I sometimes feel, in reviewing the evidence on the localization of the memory trace, that the necessary conclusion is that learning just is not possible. . . . It is not possible to demonstrate the isolated localization of a memory trace anywhere within the nervous system." (F. A. Beach et al., *The Neuropsychology of Lashley*. New York: McGraw-Hill, 1960, pp. 500–501.)

Nonetheless, learning does occur, and we do remember things. But these memories—however they are stored—are not anatomically localized.

What are the substrates for memories? Is memory a dynamic process involving continued firing of neurons in reverberatory patterns; or is memory static, the result of a fixed memory trace, or engram? If it is a dynamic, continuous process, how is it kept active over the sometimes extremely long period between experience and later recall? If memory is the result of fixed memory traces, where are they fixed? These questions are difficult, and the answers require the combined efforts of psychologists, neurophysiologists, biochemists, and scientists in related disciplines. The papers that follow describe current research attempting to "locate" memories not anatomically but within the biochemical makeup of nerve cells.

How are memories recalled? Which of our myriad of experiences will be remembered and which forgotten? By what process do we recall our prior experiences? Some researchers have suggested that we have a scanning device, something like that used by computers to retrieve magnetically stored memories. D. Ewen Cameron, for instance, in "The Processes of Remembering," presents a hypothetical model to provide a tentative answer. In the opening paper on memory, neurophysiologist Ralph W. Gerard reviews the problem and presents some results from his own laboratory that pertain especially to the question of memory storage as a dynamic or static process.

WHAT IS MEMORY?*

Ralph W. Gerard

A textbook of biochemistry widely used early in this century had a famous passage on the memory of linseed oil. Exposure to light makes the oil turn gummy. A brief exposure may not cause any observable change. But on later illumination the oil will change more rapidly than if it had not already been exposed. The oil "remembers"

---

* From *Scientific American*, Vol. 189 (3), September 1953, pp. 118–126.

its past experience and behaves differently because of it. Its memory consists in the fact that light produces, among other things, substances which aid the light-induced oxidations that make it gummy.

However far removed this may be from remembering the Gettysburg address, it clearly points up one way in which memory can work —by means of material traces of the past—and the difficulty of defining what memory is. Actually the behavior of the oil and of a human being memorizing the Gettysburg address are but extremes of a spectrum of such behavior in nature. Between these extremes there is a pretty smooth continuity, and any concept which defines memory much more narrowly than "the modification of behavior by experience" will run into trouble. Consciousness, for example, is not necessary to memory, for men remember, and recall under hypnosis, innumerable details never consciously perceived.

Where, then, shall we draw the line? A pebble, rubbed smooth in a stream, rolls differently from the original angular stone. Experience has here modified behavior; the past has been stored in a changed structure. Yet this does not greatly interest us as an instance of memory. Perhaps we should restrict the notion of memory to changes in systems which participate actively in causing the change. Then linseed oil "remembers," and so does the bulging calf muscle of a ballet dancer. Does a developing embryo "remember" the major steps, and missteps, in the long evolution of the species? Do trees "remember" good and bad seasons in the thickness of their rings? Is a film a memory of light in chemicals and a tape recording a memory of sound in magnetism? Is a library a memory of thoughts in books and a brain a memory of thoughts in protoplasm? Even to identify memory, let alone explain it, is no simple matter.

Without memory the past would vanish; intelligence, often called the ability to learn by experience, would be absent, and life would indeed be "a tale told by an idiot, full of sound and fury, signifying nothing." Today the search for the fundamental mechanisms of memory in the nervous system is being pressed with hopeful enthusiasm. The smell of success is in the air and great developments seem to wait just over the next ridge.

Let us consider as memory only that exhibited in man and in such sophisticated behavior as is usually close to conscious awareness. One great problem is: Why do certain impressions become conscious upon reception while others do not; why does awareness accompany some acts, but not others; what, in general, invests certain neural events with a phosphorescence of subjective recognition? This question remains unanswered, but the answer is likely to come in terms of the evolution of awareness of certain types of neural events as useful to the organism.

Memory involves the making of an impression by an experience, the retention of some record of this impression and the re-entry of this record into consciousness (or behavior) as recall and recognition. The initial impression need not have entered awareness in order to be retained and recalled. Anyone asked to recall what he has just seen in a room or in a picture does a less complete job than a subject under hypnosis even years later. I have been told of a bricklayer who, under hypnosis, described correctly every bump and grain on the top surface of a brick he had laid in a wall 20 years before!

Guesses have been made as to how many items might be accumulated in memory over a lifetime. Some tests of perception suggest that each tenth of a second is a single "frame" of experience for the human brain. In that tenth of a second it can receive perhaps a thousand units of information, called bits. In 70 years, not allowing for any reception during sleep, some 15 trillion bits might pour into the brain and perhaps be stored there. Since this number is more than 1,000 times larger than the total of nerve cells, the problem of storage is not exactly simple.

Whether or not all incoming sensations are preserved as potential memories, there is an important time factor in their fixation. Youthful, repeated or vivid experiences seem most firmly fixed. They are the last to survive disrupting conditions—old age, brain damage, concussion or mental shock—and the first to return after a period of amnesia. A goose seems to fix upon the first moving object it sees as its mother and thereafter follows it about. An infant, suddenly frightened by a barking dog, may fear dogs for the rest of its life.

More often, experiences force themselves into attention and memory only gradually. Even learning to perceive is a long, troublesome matter. Adults gaining vision for the first time must labor for months to learn to recognize a circle and to distinguish it from a triangle, let alone to see letters and words.

After any experience, apparently, considerable time must elapse between the arrival of the incoming nerve impulses and the fixing of the trace. If a photographic plate acted similarly, it could not be developed at once after exposure but only some time later. Recent experiments in our laboratory have emphasized this phenomenon. Hamsters daily were run in a maze and were given an electric shock afterward. When the shock was given 4 hours or more after the run, it did not influence the learning curve. (The question of cumulative damage is irrelevant here.) A shock 1 hour after the run impaired learning a little, and as the shock was brought closer it interfered more and more, until at 1 minute after the run, it destroyed learning completely. Clearly, some process of fixing continues for at least an hour.

The nature of the fixing process must be left for the moment, while some related phenomena of memory are noted. One is a type of erasing. A memory wizard who can glance through a newspaper and then name the word at any position in any column on any page makes an effort to forget this mass of information at the close of a performance so as not to "clutter up" his memory. Perhaps similar is the removal by a presuggested signal of an instruction to a hypnotized subject to perform some act after arousal. In such instances stored experience traces seem to be expunged, but whether they are really irrecoverable is perhaps not fully established. Recall alone may be at fault, as in simple forgetting.

A second phenomenon has to do with the alteration of memory traces. The memory left by an experience can change progressively. Memory, as has been well said, is reconstructive rather than reduplicative. It is also highly associative. Pictures redrawn from memory at intervals become more regular (details are smoothed out) or more exaggerated (some salient feature is caricatured) or an object different from the original (a chair looks more like a horse at each redrawing).

Besides fixation and storage, there remain recall and recognition. Failure to recall does not imply loss of the trace: witness the frequent experience of temporary inability to say a familiar name "just on the tip of my tongue." The most intriguing problem about memory, however, is not the existence but the tremendous specificity of recall. Both in its positive and negative aspects—as seen in dreams, in amnesia, in suppression and repression, in hypnosis, in hysteria and dual personality—recall offers bizarre phenomena, formidable to explain.

One day not long ago, as I left a lecture room, I caught a fleeting glimpse of the head and shoulders of a person half-silhouetted against a window over 100 feet away. I knew at once with certainty the name of the person standing there, although he had not crossed my path nor his name my mind for more than 15 years. A chord, a note, a word, a line can recall a long-past experience. Or it may reawaken an intense emotion without the connected experience; I know of a young man who invariably faints at the sight of a stethoscope, yet he has no general fear of doctors or illness and no idea of why he reacts so uncontrollably.

Recall may sometimes be disguised, seemingly to protect the subject from the anguish of fear or shame or pain. Parts of a story that touch upon a personal problem are often "forgotten" only to appear, modified, in a dream. A man who was unable to recall the telephone number of a girl friend while visiting her city dreamed of red objects that night and recognized in the morning that the numerical positions of the letters r, e, d in the alphabet gave the missing number. This opens the door to the whole edifice of symbols. An unsophisticated youngster, directed under hypnosis to dream about bed-wetting, may report his dream in Freudian symbols which only an experienced psycho-analyst—or another naive youngster under hypnosis!—can recognize as referring to bed-wetting.

Finally, what of the compulsive neurotic whose affliction is banished when some infant experience is dredged up during psychotherapy? What of the psychoneurotic soldier, unable to recall a battle beyond a certain point, who relives under pentothal all the horror of seeing a companion's head blown off and is then able to remember and talk about it? What of aphasics, who can recognize words by sight or by sound but not both? And what of dream experiences, not actually sensed but presumably due to intrinsic brain activity, which may be recalled in wakefulness or only in other dreams, if at all? The problem of recall and its specificity is the real challenge to neuro-physiology.

The human brain is composed of some 10 billion nerve cells, more or less alike, which interact in various ways. Each cell contributes to behavior, and presumably to mental activity, by firing impulses or failing to fire. All the phenomena of memory must be explained in terms of the temporal and spatial patterns of these discharges.

If experience is to modify behavior, the activity of neurons connected with an experience must alter their subsequent activity patterns. Two general questions regarding the neural trace must be asked, and both can be given a reasonable, if not a certain, answer today. The first is: Does memory depend on a continuing activity or on some static residue, some structural alteration, left behind by past activity? Is a river the water flowing in it or the channel the water cuts? The answer today is tending strongly toward the latter. The second question is: Is the structural trace (or dynamic process) for each memory located in a particular region, or are memory traces suffused through the brain in some way? Are memories marks placed on violin strings or are they wave trains playing over these strings? The latter would imply dynamic memory, but the trace could still be structural, like the wiggled groove on a phonograph record. Whether the trace is localized or diffuse, its exact nature is a third, if somewhat subsidiary, question. Current investigations suggest that there are multiple patterns of local traces rather than a single well-localized one, but the nature of the trace is almost pure guess.

A dynamic memory would depend on the continuous passage of nerve impulses or on the maintenance of some active metabolic or potential change in neurons, presumably reinforced by the repeated arrival of impulses. A nerve impulse traveling around a closed loop of connecting neurons would be a mechanism for such a dynamic memory, each remembered item depending on the activity of a particular loop or net of neurons. (Actually, since there are more memories than neurons, different memories would have to share portions of the same path, but this is physiologically possible without snarling traffic.) Such a memory device would, however, be metabolically expensive, and if the impulses really left no long-enduring trace, memories would be completely and irrevocably lost once the activity stopped.

There is a simple way to test the question as to whether a memory is purely dynamic. One need only stop all nerve impulses in the brain momentarily and observe whether a memory is lost. The problem, of course, is to stop the impulses reversibly. In sleep or under anesthesia the brain slows down but remains electrically active, and memories are largely undisturbed. But the brain's electrical activity can be stopped in several ways. When a hibernating animal, such as the hamster, is cooled to a body temperature of 40 degrees Fahrenheit, needles thrust into its brain fail to pick up electrical activity; it seems reasonably certain that the reverberating impulses are frozen in their tracks.

Another way of stopping the circulating nerve messages is to stimulate the neurons simultaneously by a vigorous electric shock, so that all the neurons presumably are unable to respond to a normal impulse. Such a shock does produce a period of complete electrical silence, measured in seconds or minutes. If the lower brain, controlling respiration, is included, the normal messages for breathing are suspended. Brain neurons may also be made electrically inactive by withholding oxygen for some 2 minutes or by withholding sugar. In all these cases the animals recover rapidly after the temporary treatment, and their memory can be investigated.

The experiment is now straightforward. Hamsters are first taught a simple maze. They are then hibernated or given electric shock or made to breathe nitrogen for a few minutes. After recovering, they are tested for their retention of learning. If they remember the way through the maze, the memory did not depend upon reverberating circuits or upon any other purely dynamic process. They remember!

This by no means excludes the initial dependence of memory on neuron activity. The passage of impulses is necessarily involved in the initial experience that leaves a memory trace. The fact that repetition makes for better memory reminds us of the analogy of the river cutting a channel in its bed. Indeed, the reason it takes time to fix a memory trace in the brain may be that impulses must circulate over their selected pathways many times in order to leave behind an enduring material change.

What, then, is this enduring static trace? Muscle fibers react to continued exercise by increasing their content of hemoglobin-like pigment; the meat becomes darker. No one has described an enduring chemical change in nerve or brain as a result of activity, but it must be conceded that this is a difficult quest that has not been undertaken very seriously. Muscle fibers swell and become hypertrophied on exercise. It has been shown recently that nerve fibers also swell slightly as they conduct impulses, and the swelling persists at least for minutes and hours if not for days and years. Nerve fibers also show alterations in potential which outlast the active period by many minutes. Any of these changes might occur at the critical junction between one neuron and the next—the synapse or gap across which conduction is considerably more precarious than it is along the uniform nerve fiber. The change might then make the passage of subsequent impulses easier or more difficult.

Certain it is that activity can facilitate and inactivity hinder the subsequent passage of an impulse across a synapse. This has been learned from experiments on simple spinal cord reflexes involving only one sensory neuron, one synapse and one motor neuron in each arc. If some of the sensory nerve fibers serving the knee-jerk reflex are stimulated, say 100 times a second for 10 minutes, and are then tested with a single stimulus, the number of motor fibers responding (in effect, the size of the knee-jerk) is increased tenfold above the normal response to a single shock. The increased responsiveness dies out in two or three phases, one lasting for seconds and one certainly for hours. This suggests that the local trace left behind may have involved several changes. Conversely, when impulses are prevented from reaching the synapses of this reflex for days or weeks, by cutting the sensory nerve connections, the reflex elicited by a single shock is strikingly below normal. After a few shocks, however, the response begins to improve, and again the return toward normal seems to involve more than one phase.

Many suggestions have been made as to what kinds of changes may alter the response at a synapse. They must be structural—either in the fibers and contacts or at the molecular level, where displacement of ions might alter the electric potential or displacement of atoms change the chemistry. One observed change, already noted, is the swelling of fiber end-bulbs induced by activity. The swelling should favor the transmission of impulses. Actually this explanation is a modern version of one of the earliest theories of memory: that activity somehow causes a nerve fiber to sprout new twigs near its termination and so to increase its effective contact. Neurons from brains of older persons have in fact been reported to branch more extensively than those from the young, and the notoriously poor memory of old people for recent events might be attributed to the neurons' inability to grow more twigs or to accommodate more connections. A closely related suggestion, that electric-shock treatment of some psychoses is successful because it destroys certain existing connections and permits neurons to make "healthier" ones, is based upon the observation, made on transparent tadpole tails, that electric shocks cause nerve filaments to be torn off.

Another mechanism enjoying some current popularity is chemical. Since every type of cell of every individual of every species has its own chemical personality, and since this differentiation of cells depends on proteins, the specificity of memory might be due to changes in nerve proteins. Each trace could be limited to one or a few molecules in an end-bulb of a neuron. The body cells that manufacture and release antibodies against invading organisms "learn," as we know, from experience. When typhoid proteins, for instance, enter the body the first time, antibodies are produced slowly and in small amounts. But years later, when almost no antibody remains in the blood, a new invasion by this specific protein is met by a prompt and vigorous release of antibody that nips the disease before it gets started.

It is far from explained just how the passage of nerve impulses would alter protein molecules at a synapse, or how, in turn, an altered protein composition would aid or hinder the passage of a nerve impulse. Yet some such chemical mechanism cannot be discarded, for nerves and synapses can be highly specific and can change their specificity. For example, if an extra muscle is transplanted into the back of a salamander, the nerve to which it becomes attached will make the transplanted muscle contract simultaneously with the normal flexor if the transplant is a flexor muscle or with the normal extensor if it is an extensor. Somehow the central synapses have "discovered" what kind of muscle is attached at the far end of the motor neuron and they let through nerve impulses at the proper time for a muscle of this sort.

The essence of all these suggested mechanisms is that a given end-bulb of a neuron, initially ineffective, can become and remain effective as a result of activity. Indeed, mathematical theories of the behavior of complex nerve nets demand only such an assumption to account for the basic properties of memory. Moreover, the total number of end-bulbs on the neurons of the brain, some 10 trillion, about matches the number of bits of information the brain may store during a lifetime. But then each memory would have to have its exact microscopic spot in the brain, would have to stay put through life, and would somehow have to be deposited, once and once only, at a given end-bulb, despite the wide sweep of impulses through the brain during each experience. This raises sharply the problem of localization.

The degree of localization is probably the key problem of memory. If we could expect to find a given memory at a given place in the brain, our experimental problem would be comparatively simple. We would locate the region and compare structural, chemical or physical changes there in animals with and without the appropriate experience. Some years ago there was an exciting report that electrical stimulation of a small spot in the cerebral cortex caused trained dogs to make a conditioned leg movement, while in unconditioned or deconditioned animals the same region was inactive. Alas, this claim has not been substantiated. There is, however, valid evidence of a kind of memory localization. When the exposed brain of a person under local anesthesia for a brain operation is stimulated electrically, various conscious effects are produced. Stimulating the occipital lobe, which receives the sensory fibers from the eyes, gives visual sensations. Similarly, stimulation of other specific regions produces sounds and skin sensations. These responses are not related to specific past experiences. However, other regions of the brain, particularly the temporal lobe, do respond to stimulation with the conscious recall of quite specific events from an individual's past.

The particularity, however, is at best only roughly localized, and localization largely vanishes when we look at the effects of brain damage. Large sections of nearly any part of the brain can be destroyed without loss of particular memories or, indeed, without disturbance of the memory function. Human brains have been extensively damaged by trauma, by tumors or abscesses, by loss of circulation, by operative removal, or by the shriveling away of extreme age. In these cases the ability to learn new things, to make sound judgments, to see new relations and to imagine new ideas may be profoundly disturbed, but the recollection of past experience is likely to remain reasonably intact. The frontal lobes of mental patients would not be amputated so freely as they are today if any serious defect in memory resulted.

So we are left with good reasons for believing that memories depend on static changes left behind by the passage of nerve impulses; that these changes occur somewhere along the paths the impulses traveled and are most likely at particular synapses; that the traces are to some extent gathered in certain regions, but that extensive brain damage is not accompanied by comparable losses of memories. One line of escape from the dilemma is to assume, as we can quite reasonably, that a given memory is not represented by one specific local change but by a pattern of many changed loci—a pattern with sufficient redundancy so that if part of it is destroyed the rest will still suffice to represent the memory.

Such a view raises serious difficulties, but they do not appear to be insurmountable. For example, if thousands of neuron endings are involved in one memory, how can the brain store the huge number of memories we have assumed? Actually, such indirect coding could greatly increase its storage capacity. Ten letters, each used to represent one item, give 10 items; but 10 letters used in groups as words give a vast number of items. Such patterned memory traces might also actually change with time, as particular neurons or synapses dropped out of the ensemble, and so permit the alteration of memories observed on successive recalls.

We come finally to the problem of recall. Recall is a matter of attention, a selecting or rejecting of particular memory traces. Here enter all the intriguing phenomena of specificity, suppression, symbolization and the like. The physiological explanation of these is certainly not yet at hand. Perhaps the best clue now available is the control of cortical activity and of conscious awareness by nerve centers in the older and deeper parts of the nervous system. Much recent experimentation has shown that these primitive jumbled masses of nerve cells in the upper part of the brain stem exercise a profound influence on the more recently evolved neurons of the cerebral cortex. Impulses from these deep cell groups continuously spray out to the cortex to regulate its activity. An excess of stimulation leads to cortical overactivity and convulsive seizures, followed by the unconsciousness of exhausted neurons. When the impulses are few and the cortex is comparatively inactive, the brain waves slow down and normal sleep results. One is tempted by the picture of an electron beam scanning the tube face of a television camera, picking up impressions left by the outside world from one tiny region after another. But whether such beams of nerve impulses, playing upon the cortex, do actually control attention, whether they are responsible for the evocation of specific memory traces, only the future can decide.

We are beginning to have some reasonable guesses as to the "gadgets" that would serve as a memory mechanism—guesses sufficiently concrete to permit testing by rigorous experimentation. I think it is realistic to hope for an understanding of memory precise enough to permit experimental modification of it in men.

Gerard's article provides a basic understanding of the problem of memory mechanisms. The following selection, by psychiatrist D. Ewen Cameron, shows a somewhat different picture, one which emphasizes the recent evidence regarding the possible role of nucleic acids in memory.

THE PROCESSES OF REMEMBERING*

D. Ewen Cameron

In his *Physiology of Mind,* published in 1876, Maudsley had already seized upon the fact of the cardinal position that memory plays in the total behaviour of man. He pointed out that "No mental development would be possible without it. For if a man possessed it not, he would be obliged to begin his conscious life fresh with each impression made upon him and would be incapable of any education." He also foresaw—although the immense range of data which we now possess was lacking to him—that it is not images or ideas of objects that are stored, but rather changes in some organic substrate of the brain. He recognized, in a word, that "coding" takes place and, indeed, he saw this long before that phrase had been coined. He was clearly and profoundly interested in the process with which many of us are presently concerned, namely the retrieval of stored information.

The word "remembering" covers not one but a multiplicity of functions. They lie in a long range and are varied in nature. First and most commonly thought of as remembering are those functions which serve

* Reprinted from *The British Journal of Psychiatry,* Vol. 109, 1963, pp. 325–340. By permission. Copyright © 1963 by the Royal Medico-Psychological Association.

our needs for precise recovery of information in the exact form in which it was laid down—an address, a formula, a date. Then we pass over to the curious, evolving, moving, changing kind of remembering which is required for the learning of a skill. This kind of remembering allows us to replace one modification by the next and almost always to produce in response to the same cue the most recent modification. An excellent example is furnished by the learning of a new top-spin drive in tennis.

Passing on to the far end of the range, we find lying there those memorial functions which permit us to change our recollections of the past so that the past becomes more endurable, more reconcilable with the image of ourselves which we find at least tolerable. These functions appear to be governed by our emotions and by the re-moulding powers exercised by our ongoing concept of ourselves and of our world. So we come to forget that we stole from our mother's purse as a child, or we may discover—like Darwin building his theory of the origin of species—that unless we are careful immediately to record as they occur all ideas contrary to the theory, they are remarkably soon forgotten.

Intelligence may be the pride—the towering distinction of man; emotion gives colour and force to his actions; but memory is the bastion of his being. Without memory, there is no personal identity, there is no continuity to the days of his life. Memory provides the raw material for designs both small and great. Thus, governed and enriched by memory, all the enterprises of man go forward.

. . . Memory has become within the last few years one of the great areas of intensive study. Promise murmurs from the pioneering laboratories that matters concerning remembering—over which mankind has pondered for 1,500 years by record—may be on their way to solution.

What are these basic problems of remembering? Let me first state them as they were considered by the Greeks. Plato (Grassi, 1959) around 354 B.C. was deeply concerned as to how memory traces were formed and stored. He advanced the idea that there is an analogy between this and the process of imparting an impression to a block of wax. He saw that the wax impression and the memory trace share a common destiny—in some cases quickly fading—sometimes being preserved throughout a lifetime—or yet again being misplaced for moments, for days or forever. Other Greeks raised the question of how memories are retrieved. Or again, what is the difference, if any, between knowledge when it is first recorded and the same knowledge later recalled?—clearly our own problem, stated in other words, of secondary elaboration. And finally, the Greeks wondered how memory is related to that elusive faculty—our sense of time.

With our vastly increased store of information about the human organism, we have been able, as a first step, to sharpen and reshape these questions. Let me state them in terms of three great areas of enquiry, each containing hardly less important questions within it.

The first is one which in far earlier times could not be set up because of the lack of anatomical knowledge. This is, where in the brain are memory traces recorded and stored? The second great area of enquiry is, what is it that serves as a substrate for memory? What is the substance which, like Plato's wax block, actually receives and holds the memory trace? The third area of search is, how does the machinery of the memorial process work? How do we perform this great range of functions—coding and decoding precision of recall, evolving recall as required in skills and the greatly modified recall of otherwise unacceptable memory traces?

Within this vast and vastly intricate area there lie the questions of the nature of retrieval, the curious enigma of the differing ease of recognition and recall, the mechanisms of retroactive and proactive inhibition and the intriguing phenomena of anterograde and posterograde amnesia. Here too, lie the fascinating puzzles of how the incoming sensory impulses are coded for recording and how, on retrieval, this coding is converted into the data of consciousness—the process of readout.

Now let us look down on to these three great areas of exploration, follow the men at work in them, see what tools they are using, note what they have now discovered, and trace their plans for further exploration.

In the first area at which we look—the arena where men are working to discover where memory traces are recorded and brought to their final storage areas—there still remains great confusion and contradiction. This confusion is characteristic of a great, wide-flung research area in which all the facts have not yet been found; all the connections between the intricate array of findings have not yet been traced out.

A long series of men worked in this field all throughout the 19th century. During this period the clinical neurologists took the lead—men, such as Prochaska and Gall, who sought to find where memories are stored in the brain chiefly on the basis of their clinical findings. Theory took form largely under the leadership of Flechsig and favoured the localized storage of memories.

These workers were later supported by growing advances made by the conditioned-reflex school. The claims of Pavlov and his co-workers, however, were made without actual neurological and neurosurgical experimental evidence. For the Pavlovians, the assumption that memories were stored in association areas served simply to complete the structure of their basic theory.

A beginning sophistication in the concept of the storage of memory traces appeared with the discoveries of Henry Head (1926) and Kurt Goldstein (1939), who showed that the disturbances found in aphasia and agnosia are not true failures in remembering, but defects in the categorization of ideas. Early in the twentieth century, the lead in the search for the location of the storage of memory traces was increasingly taken by the animal experimentalists and, in particular, by those who based their experiments upon surgical procedures. For by these means, it was possible to study the function of one part of the brain after another with respect to the memorial process. The work of the animal experimenters reached the point of greatest penetration in the researches of Lashley (1950).

In 1950, Lashley summarized his work in an article entitled "In Search of the Engram." This report exercised profound influence upon the thinking of men working in this field, and its effects are still felt. He concluded that it was not possible to demonstrate specific localization of the memory trace anywhere within the nervous system and definitively declared that the association areas are not storehouses for particular memories.

Lashley considered that the memory trace is recorded by means of multiple representations. He postulated that the nervous network may develop a pattern of activity by the spread of excitation much as the surface of a liquid develops an interference pattern of spreading waves when it is disturbed at various points. This, he felt, would result in the neurons being sensitized to react in certain combinations, perhaps in complex patterns of reverberatory circuits reduplicated throughout the area. Furthermore, he gave consideration to the number of cells in the brain and concluded that all of the cells must be in almost constant activity; that there is no excess of cells which can be used for the preservation of special memories. He concluded further that recall involves the synchronized action of a very large number of neurons.

His long series of researches were of particular value in bringing to the fore not only this fundamental conception, but also in making clear that much of what previously had been taken as a disturbance in the storage of memory traces was actually a disturbance in closely linked but not identical functions—such as in failure in shifting from one task to another or in difficulty in maintaining a constant set while endeavouring to remember a task. And he supported the views of Henry Head and Kurt Goldstein, who, as we have already pointed out, showed that aphasia and agnosia are to be considered as primary defects in the organization of ideas rather than as representing the loss of memory traces.

Hardly had this monumental and apparently conclusive report been published than it was challenged by evidence brought forward by the neurosurgeons. For, with the coming of the mid-century, information derived from operative procedures on the human subject became at once much more abundant and far more reliable. It was more reliable for two reasons: the first is that increasingly refined and efficient techniques permitted operations to be carried out on parts of the human brain into which the neurosurgeons previously could not venture. The second is that part of the evidence was derived from varieties of the lobotomy operation, which was then reaching its acme of application. This operation was carried out on brains which, if they could not be described as entirely healthy, were at least free from massive and pervasive pathologies such as traumatic change, abscesses or tumors.

Williams and Pennypacker (1954) reported a Korsakoff type of memory deficit occurring in individuals who had lesions in the hypothalamic region. They were followed by a number of workers (Scoville and Milner, 1957; Whitty and Lewin, 1957, 1960; Sweet, Talland, and Ervin, 1959) who rapidly defined a specific area which when bilaterally damaged results in a persistent failure of recent memory and an immediate retrograde amnesia of at least several weeks. The area thus defined is the hippocampal-fornix-mammillary system.

A rather interesting light on the possible specificity of localization was thrown by the work of Penfield (1952) on electrical stimulation of the temporal lobe. Discussing the memory changes following bilateral hippocampal lesions, Penfield has suggested that they interfere with memory recording, and that already established skills are not interfered with. It is probably premature, however, to come to this conclusion inasmuch as one cannot say to what extent the damage is in the retrieval mechanism rather than in the recording mechanism. However, it is quite possible to state that there may not be such a discordance between the views of Lashley and the reports of these more recent workers, since this system, namely the hippocampal-fornix-mammillary body circuit, might simply be an essential pathway to the general areas of the brain where memories are recorded and from which they are retrieved.

Another attack on this apparent enigma presented by these contrasting findings of Lashley and the neurosurgeons has been made by those who consider that recording is a two-stage procedure. Teuber (1962), for instance, has recently stated, "A focal process of initial registration and consolidation precedes a subsequent dispersal involving large portions of the cerebral hemisphere." In the electroshock procedure, we have a means of producing graduated amnesia, and it is of interest to note that there is a proportional relationship between the number of electroshocks given within a period of time and the extent of the amnesias. It is quite possible, for instance, to produce a long-lasting, probably permanent, amnesia by setting the number of electroshock treatments to be given within a predetermined period. Those of us who have worked on this . . . take the view that this phenomenon cannot readily be understood in terms of consolidation, but can be more easily grasped if we consider that the longer a memory trace exists, the more connections it develops with other traces. From here we may go on to postulate that those memory traces with numerous, long-established interconnections are much less easily obliterated than those of recent origin. This criticism of the concept of consolidation leaves intact the possibility that recording may be in the form of a two-stage operation, as already described.

We may now leave this first great area, namely, the location where memory traces are recorded and stored, with at least the temporary assumptions that they are widely stored throughout the brain and that the hippocampal-fornix-mammillary system probably plays an important part in the conveying of the neural impulses to and from the storage areas.

We now turn to the second great area of enquiry: What serves as the organic substrate for the memory trace? For a considerable time it has been considered that memories are preserved in the brain in the form of traces which are laid down at the time the experience occurs and which are reactivated at the moment of remembering.

Earlier workers, in attempting to provide on theoretic grounds a substrate for the trace, tended to put forward one of several hypotheses. The first was that the trace is laid down in terms of alteration at the synapse; a modification of this was that it is laid down in terms of the linking together of a network of neurons. The third one, which deviated relatively little from the first two, was that the trace is laid down in terms of altered conductivity.

It was not until 1947 that an entirely new concept arose. This was that the memory trace is laid down in terms of changes in cell protein. This new concept sprang into being with the discovery that the protein structure of neural cells is exceedingly complex and that it also varies from cell to cell. This at last provided what had been sought, namely, a substrate of sufficient complexity to permit the recording of the exceptionally large number of bits of information which the individual possesses in the form of memories.

Katz and Halstead (1950) stated the concept in these terms: "Neurons involved in memory become fully functional only after chemical structural changes"; and they suggested that a neuron becomes operative in virtue of the formation of a new, specifically oriented, protein molecule. They assumed that the molecule was a nucleoprotein and that it acted as a template for the synthesis of protein replicas.

From this point onwards, a number of workers entered this field, of whom the most active has been Hydén (1955). He advanced the hypothesis that the substrate is ribonucleic acid and pointed out that in the many combinations permitted by the rearrangement of its four bases, one has a substance which in principle could encode 10^{15} or more bits of information. He set up a theory as to how the pattern of nerve impulses entering the cell could determine the stability of one of the four bases at a given site on a pre-existing RNA molecule. He was not, however, able to demonstrate this experimentally.

Interest in this theory spread rapidly. Morrell (1961), using a technique whereby the production of an artificial epileptogenic area in the cortex of one hemisphere could produce a mirror epileptogenic area on the cortex of the opposite hemisphere in the same general area, demonstrated that this resulted in unusually high concentrations of ribonucleic acid in the abnormally discharging mirror focus.

Despite this interest, experimentation on the human subject was strangely absent. In 1956, when we commenced our studies of the role of RNA in the memorial process of aged individuals, so great were the ranges of scientific literature that we were quite unaware of the earlier conjectures of Katz and Halstead. So, if the early theorists and microbiochemists seemed unaware of the possibilities offered by human investigation, those of us who were experienced in this field were equally unaware of those stimulating ideas which had grown up in the shadow of larger speculations concerning the structure of proteins and the micrometabolism of cells.

For over 20 years we had been working in an attempt to find some substance which would correct the memory deficit found in the aged. In 1955, Paul Weiss made a report summarizing his work on the neuron in the previous several decades. It was a singularly stimulating report. He pointed out that the neuron—far from being a fixed or relatively static structure—is constantly in action, and that in particular it is continually producing material at the nucleated end which passes along, disappearing as it goes, towards the terminal structure of the axon. In a subsequent review of the work of himself and others (Weiss, 1961), using both this axon-damming method and radioactive isotope tracers, he estimated that the flow occurred at the rate of 2–3 mm. a day. Since there was some evidence that the substances might include the nucleic acids, as suggested by the earlier work of Hydén (1950) and Samuels et al. (1951), it was decided to start exploring the use of the nucleic acids in the human subject.

It seemed reasonable, seeing that DNA is primarily found in the nucleus, to start with it. We used this primarily in oral form, but to a limited extent also in intravenous form, and got no results. We then turned to ribonucleic acid (RNA), both in oral and intravenous form, and began at least with the former to get definite although limited evidence of amelioration of memory deficits in the aged individuals we were studying. However, the earlier intravenous solutions were so apt to produce severe shock-like reactions, that they were stopped.

We continued improving oral administration, and as we did so and could give larger and larger amounts, we began to be increasingly certain that in a growing number of cases we were able to produce changes which could be recorded and statistically evaluated by the test instruments which we had devised—notably the counting test (Cameron, 1943), certain parameters of the conditioned reflex procedure (Solyom and Beach, 1961) and the Wechsler Memory Quotient.

In 1961, Dr. S. Sved, who had joined the biochemical side of our investigative team, was able to produce a greatly improved solution of RNA for intravenous use. This solution yielded much more rapid and much more extensive results and we were now able to differentiate between the responsiveness of three categories of patients showing organic brain deficits, namely, presenile, arteriosclerotic and senile (Cameron, Solyom, Sved, and Wainrib, 1962).

The procedure which we presently follow calls for extensive pretreatment evaluation, in which we employ the counting test, the Wechsler Memory Quotient and the following parameters of the conditioned reflex procedure which have been developed by Dr. Solyom of our research team into methods for estimation of memory change:

(a) Rate of extinction of the orienting reflex;
(b) Speed of acquisition of a conditioned reflex;
(c) Rate of retention of the conditioned reflex;
(d) Rate of extinction of the conditioned reflex;
(e) Capacity for discrimination between conditioned stimuli;
(f) Capacity to delay a conditioned reflex.

We now employ, as well, two types of a time-estimation test as developed for us by Mr. Claude Beaulieu of our research group. The first is based on asking the individual to state when 5, 10, 15 and 30 seconds have passed from the time that a given sound was heard, and the second is based on presenting the individual with given intervals of time and asking him to estimate how many seconds he feels they represent.

We have also started to explore dichotic memory tests, which involve passing a different signal in simultaneously through each ear and asking the individual to repeat them. This test, originally evolved by Broadbent (1958), is based on the fact that one ear habitually shows itself to be dominant and therefore the data passed through the other ear must be held transiently in a memory storage system. The test is essentially one to show the efficiency of this storage system.

Along with the data, we record the electroencephalogram and collect a great deal of reportorial information through the medical staff and the social workers—the material being obtained both from the patient and his relatives. Furthermore, we are in the process of developing an occupational therapy battery to assess memory change.

Once these procedures have gone forward and once the dimensions and nature of the patient's memory deficit are defined, we select only those patients whose deficit is relatively stationary and who are not suffering from mood disorders or any serious physical condition which might in any way disturb the memorial capacity of the individual.

The subject is then given RNA in a 10 per cent buffered solution, the basic material being obtained from yeast. We have employed a variety of intravenous procedures. First we used a low concentration method whereby 10 grams of RNA in a 10 per cent solution were added to 1,000 cc. of normal saline and given by slow drip over 6–8 hours. A second method has been to administer 10 grams of RNA in a 10 per cent solution undiluted over a period of 50 minutes. These injections were usually given three times per week. A third procedure has been to give 1 gram of RNA in a 10 per cent solution twice a day. The advantage of the first is that side-effects are kept down to a minimum. The advantage of the second is to secure a high concentration of RNA and its breakdown products in the blood, and the advantage of the third is to provide a more continuous (i.e., daily) administration of RNA and at the same time to avoid the side-effects. Our more recent studies, however, suggest that the first procedure is preferable.

The side-effects referred to consist primarily in nausea and abdominal discomfort, in cramping sensations in the extremities and in a fall in blood pressure. The severity of the side-effects is related to the speed of injection. The fall in blood pressure can be corrected by pressor agents such as aramine.

Montanari, Cutolo, and Mazzoni (1961), using ribonucleotides in oral form, reported confirmation of our results.

After accumulating a considerable number of cases, we have found it possible to say that the best results are obtained in individuals whose memory disturbance is on an arteriosclerotic basis, the second group is that of the presenile, Alzheimer's and Pick's disease types, and the third group is the senile. In all three categories, the best results are obtained where the cases are treated in the early stages of memory defect.

In the meantime, other types of experimentation were now going forward which brought further evidence to support the hypothesis that ribonucleic acid is the substrate for memory. Certain of these approaches have already been discussed, and of the additional approaches the first was a group of experiments carried out in the cancer field with a pyrimidine analogue—6-azauracil. Work with this agent was initiated by Hakala, Law, and Welch (1956). When transferred to the human subject by Wells, Ajmone-Marsan, Frei, and Touhy (1957), it was found that in addition to marked changes occurring in the brainwave picture, such as the abolition of fast rhythms, the disorganization of background activity, irregular slowing and the disappearance of the response to photic stimulation, behavioural changes also appeared in the form of lethargy, somnolence, confusion and semi-coma. These changes were reversible. No work has yet appeared, however, reporting that attempts to measure the presumably accompanying memory deficits have been carried out.

Related studies have been carried forward with reference to the effects of ribonuclease upon the ability to retain a learned pattern of behavior. Later, Dingman and Sporn (1961), working with rats and studying the effect on maze learning, used an analogue, namely 8-azaguanine, and found that the capacity to learn was severely interfered with. Similar results were reported by Koenig (1960) with respect to a pyrimidine analogue.

In still another area, a quite different kind of attack was being made upon the problem of the relation of RNA to remembering. Mc-Connell, Jacobsen, and Kimble (1959) and Corning and John (1961), experimenting with the effects of ribonuclease (which breaks down ribonucleic acid) upon planarians, reported the following interesting experiment: Planarians can be trained to run a very simple T-maze. If the planarians are then transected and allowed to regenerate in ordinary pond water, both the part which regenerates from the head and that which regenerates from the tail end will show a capacity to run the maze. If, however, the head ends and the tail ends are regenerated in a solution of ribonuclease, the head ends still show a capacity to run the maze equal to that of the head or tail section which was regenerated in pond water, but the tails perform randomly.

Again shifting the basis of attack, we find that in 1960 Hydén and Pigon, working with rabbits, reported that ribonucleic acid concentrations rise in neurons during activity and perhaps during learning, and that after such activity a decreased amount is to be found in the neurons but an increased amount in the glial cells surrounding the neurons. In other words, their basic suggestion is that ribonucleic acid increases in amount in neurons during activity, and their second suggestion is that the glial cells possibly play a much more active part in cerebral activity and perhaps in memory than has hitherto been supposed. They consider that these findings give further support to the contention that the substrate of remembering is ribonucleic acid.

This may be the answer to a difficult question, namely, if the contents of the neuron are constantly streaming towards the end of the axon, how is it possible to ensure the maintenance of a fixed memory trace? However, this suggestion that the memory trace may actually be in the glial cells rather than in the neuron should only be taken as highly tentative, since our information concerning the contents of the neuron so streaming is based on evidence supplied by the electron microscope and also on Weiss' extraordinary earlier experiments in constricting the axon.

Still another possibility should be considered in endeavouring to understand the curious phenomenon of the continuing flow of material from the nucleated part to the peripheral end of the axon and the dilemma which this raises in attempting to explain how a trace is maintained. This possibility is that although the basic mass of a substance in the neuron may change both in amount and in identity (although not necessarily in nature), yet, nonetheless, the trace may remain as a design of organization.

A simple illustration of this can be seen in the skin, which remains relatively constant in location and in texture but which is constantly being renewed, or in the eddy and swirl on the surface of a stream, which remain the same although the water which forms them is forever changing.

In a similar manner, it is possible that a memory trace may endure, although the original RNA which was its substrate has been replaced by a new supply. Fluctuations in the amount of RNA, such as the increase which has been described during neural activity, may be linked with working proposals regarding active forgetting. Thus it is possible that when a considerable number of new memory traces are being formed, as when we are actively experiencing, an increased amount of RNA is required, but less will be needed when those memories created by our experiencing are no longer necessary and have been eliminated by a process of active forgetting.

Countless experiments such as those on rote learning, on immediate recall, have shown that while memory traces are endlessly being formed during our waking hours—and apparently to some degree during our hours of sleep—a vastly greater proportion of them can no longer be recovered a few minutes after they have been formed.

It is, moreover, a matter of common experience that the number of bits of information which impinge upon the individual and to which he responds by forming temporary memory traces is clearly fluctuating. In turn, the individual shows considerable fluctuation in the extent to which he responds or, as one says in common language, in the extent to which he attends.

Weiss (1955), although clearly basically concerned with the presentation of his concept of perpetual neuronal growth, approaches the problem of how fixed or relatively fixed memory traces are maintained in a substratum which may be constantly moving its location and also being broken up or replaced. He points to the high rate of synthesis of proteins and of ribonucleic activity and to the continuous flow of semi-solid materials from the nucleated part of the neuron to the end of its axon. He considers that the fact that the neuronal mechanism is undergoing perpetual renewal permits of adaptive remodelling.

He cites the example of the antigen causing not only the formation of antibody molecules when it is actually present, but resulting in modifying the cells in a lasting manner so that they continue to manufacture the same specific antibodies. He suggests that in a similar way the nuclear production apparatus of the nerve cell might in response to appropriate stimulation henceforth turn to molecules having a particular configuration.

It seems not unreasonable to suggest that nerve impulses evoked by meaningful experience as they pass through the nerve cells may alter the conformation of molecules in a lasting way. One may assume that as these moleclues are reproduced they will tend to be identical with those formed by the original impulse. Here one may see the sketched-in outline of a theory serving to explain the preservation of engrams in a field which itself is constantly changing with respect to the substrate.

These things, however, remain highly speculative, and we should not close the list of possibilities without pointing to the fact that we are only now beginning to discover the presence in the neuron of a highly complicated inner structure consisting of a great variety of organelles. Among these organelles we should mention the ribosomes which are reported as possessing a particularly high RNA content. The role of the various membranes which exist within the cells is still largely unknown. Among these membranes is the endoplastic reticulum which, while located in the cytoplasm, is thought possibly to have direct communication with the nuclear membrane. These organelles, of which reference is being made only to two, constitute what Brachet (1961) has termed the "cyto-skeleton."

Finally, quite recently we ourselves have made a further step forward in so far that we have begun to examine ribonuclease in the blood of normals and of various individuals in the aged group who have memory defects. Dr. Sved of our research group has found evidence that ribonuclease is elevated in these individuals. This suggests the hypothesis that a possible factor in memory disturbance may be over-activity of ribonuclease.

As we set out on the survey of the processes of remembering, we found that over a prolonged period of time men have endeavoured to solve three great questions about these processes. The first: Where in the brain are memory traces stored? Second: What substrate is used for their storage? And the third question we will deal with in a moment.

With respect to the first two questions, however, it cannot be too strongly stated that the memorial processes cannot be understood purely on the basis of anatomical connections or of the biochemical substrate of memory. Were we to discover tomorrow that ribonucleic acid is actually the substrate of memory and were we able to demonstrate how this substrate is used for the coding of memory, we would still be confronted with the vastly intricate matter of the total functioning of the memorial process—a matter which no doubt will concern coming generations of researchers. How does the incoming stimulus produce the memory trace? What is the nature of coding? How is the trace held? What is the role of the emotional response? How does the retrieval mechanism find with such remarkable speed, and in most cases with such extraordinary accuracy, the tiny datum of information laid down in a day now far off? How are memory traces once coded then read out again?

Our third question, then, to which we now address ourselves, is by far the most comprehensive and difficult. It is—placing to one side the question of the location of the storehouse of memory and the nature of the substrate—how do we remember and forget? The questions here are numerous, complex and far from solution. They include one that is outstanding in its complexity and in its fundamental nature. For, as we consider the intricate chain which runs from perception through recording of the memory trace and back through decoding of that trace to actual conscious recall, there breaks in time and again to face us that most profound of enigmas, namely, the conversion of neurochemical events into the events of consciousness.

It is in a sense well that we should be thus confronted, since undoubtedly some of our difficulties in understanding remembering arise from our having tended to explore the anatomical, biochemical and psychological aspects of this function separately. Whereas, if the process is taken as a whole, leads developed in any one part can be of assistance in others. For instance, it is well known that a stimulus situation must last for a given time for the individual to respond by developing a memory trace. This suggests that the necessary neurochemical mechanism requires a certain period of time to operate. This in turn means that we can eliminate from our questioning any neurochemical mechanisms which take appreciably longer to complete operation.

Or, again, we may point out that repetition serves to stabilize the memory trace, as does the intensity of the meaning of the stimulus reaction. This raises conjectures as to the nature of the coding and storage procedures.

Finally, we may point to something that we shall shortly discuss in more detail, namely, that recognition is better preserved than is recall in organic memory deficits. This again makes one ask questions and perhaps serves to point our questions in given directions as to the nature of the storage of the memory trace.

In the course of our work on remembering, we have developed

a working concept of the various stages of the memorial process as they occur at the behavioural level. It should be pointed out that this is a purely provisional picture and probably bears no more relationship to the final portrayal of the stages of remembering than do the architect's initial sketches to the finally completed building. This working concept is shown in Figure 1.

STAGES OF MEMORIAL PROCESS

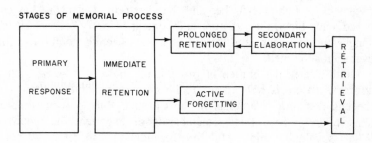

Figure 1.

I shall not attempt to deal with the links separately, but shall make some overall observations and also deal with one or two points in the process which seem particularly promising for study.

The primary response is of course an organismal event. It is based upon psychological, neurophysiological and biochemical happenings. Nonetheless, when we describe its duration, this is most easily stated in terms of its neurophysiological events. Thus we may say that the primary response is in operation during that period when the inflow of neural impulses from some stimulus commences to the point where their encoding as a memory trace is completed. Here is at once an unanswered question. Is this the course of all incoming information or does some become held in a highly transitory form for perhaps a few seconds? . . . or up to a minute or two, according to some workers, in reverberatory circuits? . . . or for periods as long as half to one hour as suggested by John (1962)?

Broadbent (1958), and Inglis and Sanderson (1961), on the basis of the former's dichotic testing procedure, have advanced a most explicit statement of memory as a two-stage procedure. And there is now a widely held belief that memory is a two-stage procedure, and hence in Figure 1 I have at least recorded a link for immediate retention and another link for prolonged retention.

The link dealing with active forgetting is more contentious, and there are those who claim, as you know, and to my mind quite absurdly, that nothing ever experienced and recalled, no matter how briefly, is ever forgotten; so that, theoretically, you should be able to remember the fifth poached egg that you ate in your life, the third person you met entering the railroad station in your home city 31 years ago, as well as the colour of the tie you wore on August 16, 1952. Moreover, quite apart from these relatively discrete events, such a theory postulates recording of every conversation heard, the frequency of lightning flashes and thunderstorms which one has endured since birth, the structure and content of every reverie, all the songs you have heard and the order of every fleeting cloud formation ever seen and noted.

Quite clearly the burden of proof is on those who assert such a concept. Nature is well known to be most parsimonious, though if the end demands it prodigal in the extreme. But no such comprehensive and indeed total remembering of experience is required. What is valuable and useful for the individual to retain—beyond the brief retention necessary to afford continuity—is strictly limited. All evidence from a great many investigators using a very considerable variety of testing procedures suggests strongly that storage space in the brain is reserved for the memory traces of matters set there under the urgency of their special emotional significance for us and maintained there because of the frequency with which such memory traces are called upon—in a word, because they are especially meaningful or they are continually useful to us.

Indeed we have some evidence of this in studies we have carried on in the last two years on perseveration. The term "perseveration" is used here in the sense that has been employed by Jaspers (1955), namely, to designate a phenomenon which is particularly apt to appear in the organic brain syndrome. This consists in the patient tending to respond to a question by means of an answer which he has just given in reply to a quite different question. Using the counting test, we found that perseveration tended to interfere with retention, that it usually appeared at the upper limits of retention, and that it could only be overcome by means of massive reinforcement of the stimulus, as where one uses multiple modalities in attaining initial registration. We considered that there are grounds for thinking that perseveration is due to a failure in the process of forgetting; in other words, that the previous question and answer had not been removed from immediate retention.

Somewhere, and probably in the section described as prolonged retention, encoding takes place. Encoding and the formation of the trace appear to us at least at the present time to be functions which are difficult to separate. As is well known, men are at this moment in the process of breaking the genetic code which employs DNA as its substrate, but we are still without a lead as to how to break the memory code which we presume is based upon RNA. It is here that the use of analogues for the bases may be of great value.

A rapidly lengthening series of reports is appearing on how encoding takes place. Most of them, however, are derived from studies of mechanical and sometimes purely theoretical information. It would also appear that those attempting these approaches are handicapped by lack of direct experience with behavioural phenomena.

May I lastly pass on to a brief consideration of what also suggests a good lead—this time to the understanding of decoding or recollection. This lead lies within the section of retrieval and consists in the comparison of the process of recall and recognition. Here one may point to the very interesting phenomenon that if one after another one puts before a patient a series of numbers, it is quite easy to demonstrate the time interval beyond which he cannot recall. If one puts before him four numbers of which one is that in quest, he will be able to recognize the correct one over a much more extended period than he can recall correctly. It would seem that in the case of recall the stream of ingoing impulses derived from the question is unable to reactivate the trace; but the trace is still there, for if this stream of ingoing impulses contains a pattern derived from the number which is being sought, it is possible to reactivate the trace. This clearly brings us to the question of how the trace is reactivated and opens the way for a series of interesting experimental approaches.

And so we complete our review of the great questions with which men have struggled from the earliest of times concerning this amazingly powerful cord which holds together all the days of our lives. Thus armed and supported, our powers infinitely amplified by all the scientific devices of our time, we draw near to the discovery of the answers to these ancient questions. We must in all humility pay tribute to the extraordinary penetration of those men who pondered these questions thousands of years ago with no devices to aid them, but fortified by the fact that if they had but one tool, it was and remains the most powerful of all—the mind of man.

REFERENCES

Brachet, J.   The living cell.   *Sci. Amer.,* 1961, **205** (3), 50–61.
Broadbent, D. E.   *Perception and communication.*   London: Pergamon, 1958.

Cameron, D. E. Impairment of the retention phase of remembering. *Psychiat. Quart.*, 1943, **17**, 395–404.

Cameron, D. E., Solyom, L., Sved, S., and Wainrib, B. Effects of intravenous administration of ribonucleic acid upon failure of memory for recent events in presenile and aged individuals. In J. Wortis (Ed.), *Recent advances in biological psychiatry*, Vol. 5. New York: Plenum, 1962. Pp. 365–374.

Corning, W. C., and John, E. R. Effect of ribonuclease on retention of conditioned response in regenerated planarians. *Science*, 1961, **134**, 1363–1364.

Dingman, W., and Sporn, M. B. The incorporation of 8-azaguanine into rat brain RNA and its effect on maze-learning by the rat: An inquiry into the biochemical basis of memory. *J. Psychiat. Res.*, 1961, **1**, 1–11.

Goldstein, K. *The organism*. New York: American Book Co., 1939.

Grassi, E. (Ed.) *Collected works of Plato*. Vol. 5. Hamburg: Rowohlt, 1959.

Hakala, M. T., Law, L. W., and Welch, A. D. Inhibitory activity of 6-azauracil, 6-uracil methyl sulfone, and related compounds on the growth of mouse lymphomas and sarcoma 180. *Proc. Amer. Ass. Cancer Res.*, 1956, **2**, 113. (abstract)

Head, H. *Aphasia and kindred disorders of speech*. Cambridge, England: Cambridge Univ. Press, 1926.

Hydén, H. Spectroscopic studies on nerve cells in development, growth and function. In P. Weiss (Ed.), *Genetic neurology*. Chicago: Univ. of Chicago Press, 1950. Pp. 177–193.

Hydén, H. Nucleic acids and proteins. In K. A. C. Elliott, I. H. Page, and J. H. Quastel (Eds.), *Neurochemistry*. Springfield, Ill.: Chas. C Thomas, 1955. Pp. 222–224.

Hydén, H., and Pigon, A. A cytophysiological study of functional relationships between oligodendroglial cells and nerve cells of Deiter's nucleus. *J. Neurochem.*, 1960, **6**, 57–72.

Inglis, J., and Sanderson, R. E. Successive responses to simultaneous stimulation in elderly patients with memory disorders. *J. abnorm. soc. Psychol.*, 1961, **62**, 709–712.

Jaspers, K. *Allgemeine psychopathologie*. Berlin: Springer Verlag, 1955.

John, E. R. Studies of memory. In F. O. Schmitt (Ed.), *Macromolecular specificity and biological memory*. Cambridge, Mass.: M.I.T. Press, 1962. Pp. 80–85.

Katz, J. J., and Halstead, W. C. Protein organization and mental function. *Comp. Psychol. Monogr.*, 1950, **20**, 1–33.

Koenig, H. Experimental myelopathy produced with a pyrimidine analogue. *A.M.A. Arch. Neurol.*, 1960, **2**, 463–475.

Lashley, K. S. In search of the engram. *Sympos. exp. Biol.*, 1950, **4**, 454–482.

McConnell, J. V., Jacobsen, A. L., and Kimble, D. P. The effects of regeneration upon retention of a conditioned response in the planarian. *J. comp. physiol. Psychol.*, 1959, **52**, 1–5.

Montanari, M., Cutolo, E., and Mazzoni, S. Acidi nucleinici e derivati: Possibili effeti sul sistema nervosa centrale e applicazioni terapeutiche in neuropsichiatria. *Arcisepedale S. Anna Ferrara*, 1961, **14**, 573–582.

Morrell, F.   Lasting changes in synaptic organization produced by continuous neuronal bombardment.   In J. F. Delafresnaye (Ed.), *Brain mechanisms and learning: A symposium.*   Oxford: Blackwell, 1961. Pp. 375–392.

Penfield, W. G., and Rasmussen, T.   *The cerebral cortex of man.*   New York: Macmillan, 1952.

Samuels, A. J., Boyarsky, L. L., Gerard, R. W., Libet, B., and Brust, M. Distribution, exchange and migration of phosphate compounds in the nervous system.   *Amer. J. Physiol.,* 1951, **164,** 1–15.

Scoville, W. B., and Milner, B.   Loss of recent memory after bilateral hippocampal lesions.   *J. Neurol. Neurosurg. Psychiat.,* 1957, **20,** 11–21.

Solyom, L., and Beach, L.   Further studies upon the effects of the administration of ribonucleic acid in aged patients suffering from memory (retention) failure.   *Neuro-psycho-pharmacol.,* 1961, **2,** 351–355.

Sweet, W. H., Talland, G. A., and Ervin, F. R.   Loss of recent memory following section of the fornix.   *Trans. Amer. neurol. Ass.,* 1959, **84,** 76–82.

Teuber, H. L.   Perspectives in the problems of biological memory: A psychologist's view. In F. O. Schmitt (Ed.), *Macromolecular specificity and biological memory.*   Cambridge, Mass.: M.I.T. Press, 1962. Pp. 99–107.

Weiss, P.   The life history of the neuron.   *Proc. Ass. Res. nerv. ment. Dis.,* 1955, **35,** 8–18.

Weiss, P.   The concept of perpetual neuronal growth and proximo-distal substance convection.   In S. S. Kety and J. Elkes (Eds.), *Regional neurochemistry.*   New York: Pergamon, 1961. Pp. 220–242.

Wells, C. E., Ajmone-Marsan, C., Frei, E., and Touhy, J. H.   Electroencephalographic and neurological changes induced in man by the administration of 1,2,4-triazine-3, 5(2H,4H)-dione (6-azauracil). *EEG clin. Neurophysiol.,* 1957, **9,** 325–332.

Whitty, C. W., and Lewin, W.   Vivid daydreaming: An unusual form of confusion following anterior cingulectomy.   *Brain,* 1957, **80,** 72–76.

Whitty, C. W., and Lewin, W.   A Korsakoff syndrome in the post-cingulectomy confusional state.   *Brain,* 1960, **83,** 648–653.

Williams, M., and Pennypacker, J.   Memory disturbances in third ventricle tumours.   *J. Neurol. Neurosurg. Psychiat.,* 1954, **17,** 115–123.

Cameron's research, using RNA in treating problems of human memory loss, suggests the possibility that memory storage consists in the modification of the molecular structure of RNA within the cells of the central nervous system. The following research report, by psychologist Leonard Cook and his colleagues, offers empirical evidence supporting this possibility. Their study found that injection of RNA yielded more rapid learning and greater resistance to extinction in rats.

RIBONUCLEIC ACID: EFFECT ON
CONDITIONED BEHAVIOR IN RATS*

**Leonard Cook, Arnold B. Davidson, Dixon J. Davis,
Harry Green, and Edwin J. Fellows**

Ribonucleic acid (RNA) derived from yeast, when chronically administered orally or intravenously, had a "favorable effect in general upon memory retention failure in the aged," particularly in patients with arteriosclerotic brain disease (Cameron, 1958; Cameron and Solyom, 1961). Treatment improved retention in a counting test, and retention and speed of reconditioning in a conditioned response procedure. In addition, this treatment increased alertness, interest, initiative, and confidence. Reduction of psychogenic confusion and improvement in memory have been reported in patients treated for cerebrovascular disease and confusional disorders (Montanari, Cutolo, and Mazzoni, 1961). Tablets containing the ribonucleotides cytidylic acid, adenlic acid, uridylic acid, and guanylic acid were administered orally each day (total 1.05 grams) for an average of 25 days.

Certain aspects of the relationship of RNA to behavioral processes in animals have been reported (Corning and John, 1961; Dingman and Sporn, 1961; John, 1961), but direct evidence that the administration of purified RNA can affect the behavior of animals is lacking. We recognize that our study may not be directly related to the reported clinical findings; however, it was designed to study the interaction of purified RNA with certain basic elements of behavior, that is, acquisition and extinction of a conditioned response in rats.

Method

Ribonucleic acid in powdered form was administered as a 10 per cent aqueous solution adjusted to pH 6.5 to 6.7. Tests were negative for pyrogenicity (by a rabbit assay) and for bacterial and mold contamination. In a preliminary investigation, rats were given 160 milligrams per kilogram (mg/kg) doses of RNA intraperitoneally

* Reprinted from *Science*, Vol. 141, July 19, 1963, pp. 268–269. By permission. Copyright © 1963 by the American Association for the Advancement of Science.

each day for 1 month; no overt symptoms were noted, and no gross pathological changes were seen in the peritoneal area upon autopsy.

Sprague-Dawley rats, 150 to 200 grams at the start of the experiment, were divided by weight into two groups of eight. One group was injected intraperitoneally each day with a 160-mg/kg dose of RNA, and the other group was similarly injected with normal saline. No significant differences in appearance or general health were apparent between groups at any time throughout either procedure, that is, over a period of more than 10 weeks, except for a slightly lower rate of weight gain in the treated group. After 53 days the rats were trained to perform a conditioned response by an established procedure (Cook and Weidley, 1957). Administration of RNA and saline to each group was continued throughout the tests. The rats were individually placed in the same position, in a chamber with an electrified grid floor, a pole suspended from the top center, and a buzzer. In unconditioned-response trials the buzzer and electric shock through the grid floor were presented simultaneously; in conditioned-response trials, only the buzzer was presented. Each trial was terminated either by a response (jumping onto the pole after onset of stimuli) or at the end of 30 seconds. Rats from each group were alternately tested in individual trials.

Results

Figure 1 (top) shows the acquisition performance curves measured by percentage of animals responding. Significant differences in performance between the treated group (group I) and the saline group were seen. In the treated group the rate of acquisition of the response was markedly faster ($P < .02$) than in the controls. Even after 100 per cent performance was achieved in both groups, the response latencies of the treated group in subsequent trials (not shown in figure) were approximately half those of the saline group.

These results were confirmed with other groups of rats (group II). The treatment was similar to that in the first experiment; however rats were tested after only 1 month. Again, the rate of acquisition of the response was significantly faster ($P < .05$) in the treated group than in the controls. When the two groups (ten rats each) achieved maximum performance, both the controls and the treated rats responded to the buzzer alone. Extinction of this conditioned response was then carried out. The treated group (group II) was more resistant to extinction than the saline group (Fig. 1, bottom). The apparent difference in the extinction rate was also statistically significant ($P < .001$).

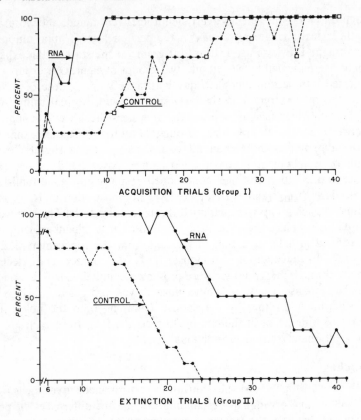

Figure 1. *Behavioral effects of RNA in rats. Dotted lines indicate averages for controls; solid lines indicate averages for treated group. (Top) Effect of 53 daily injections of RNA on acquisition of conditioned responses (group I). Circles indicate unconditioned-response trials; squares indicate conditioned-response trials. Percentage of animals of each group exhibiting the response is on ordinate; individual trials over a period of 4 days, are on abscissa. All rats received the same number of trials each day—average ten trials per day. Differences between groups (x^2) were significant at P = .05 or less (one-tailed). (Bottom) Effect on extinction after a total of 30 daily injections of RNA (group II). Conditioned stimulus was presented without shock reinforcement. Percentage of rats of each group responding to the conditioned stimulus is on ordinate; individual trials over a period of 3 days, are on abscissa. Differences between groups (x^2) were significant at P = .05 level or less (one-tailed).*

Similar results on acquisition were observed after daily treatment for 1 or 2 weeks. After 3 days of treatment no effect was observed. However, resistance to extinction was higher in the treated rats than in controls after 3 days, 1 week, 2 weeks, or 1 month of daily treatment.

Discussion

These results demonstrate that rats injected daily with RNA exhibit significantly better performance during acquisition of a conditioned response and higher resistance to extinction than rats injected with saline. We are now attempting to determine whether RNA itself, one or more of its components, degradation products, some impurity, or some biochemically resynthesized molecule is responsible for the effects described.

It is premature to conclude that the administered RNA directly affected learning or memory processes. Perhaps these measured behavioral changes are the result of the interaction of RNA with one or more of the experimental parameters utilized. However, the findings are generally consistent with some of the reported clinical results.

Summary

Acquisition of a behavioral response motivated by shock was enhanced in rats chronically treated with yeast ribonucleic acid, and resistance to extinction was greater in rats so treated than in controls. This extends the role of ribonucleic acid to include a behavioral effect in laboratory mammals treated with a purified preparation from yeast.

REFERENCES

Cameron, D. E.   The use of nucleic acid in aged patients with memory impairment. *Amer. J. Psychiat.,* 1958, **114,** 943.

Cameron, D. E., and Solyom, L.   Effects of ribonucleic acid on memory. *Geriatrics,* 1961, **16,** 74–81.

Cook, L., and Weidley, E.   Behavioral effects of some psychopharmacological agents. *Ann. N.Y. Acad. Sci.,* 1957, **66,** 740–752.

Corning, W. C., and John, E. R.   Effect of ribonuclease on retention of conditioned response in regenerated planarians. *Science,* 1961, **134,** 1363–1364.

Dingman, W., and Sporn, M. B.   The incorporation of 8-azaguanine into rat brain RNA and its effect on maze-learning by the rat: An inquiry into the biochemical basis of memory. *J. psychiat. Res.,* 1961, **1,** 1–11.

John, E. R.   High nervous functions: Brain functions and learning. *Ann. Rev. Physiol.,* 1961, **23,** 451–484.

Montanari, M., Cutolo, E., and Mazzoni, S.   Acidi nucleinici e derivati: Possibili effeti sul sistema nervosa centrale e applicazioni terapeutiche in neuropsichiatria.   *Arcisepedale S. Anna Ferrara,* 1961, **14,** 573–582.

Much theorizing and a small amount of empirical research are available about the possible role of nucleic acids in memory storage. Neurochemists Wesley Dingman and Michael B. Sporn evaluate the evidence.

MOLECULAR THEORIES OF MEMORY*

Wesley Dingman and Michael B. Sporn

Recently there has been a surge of interest, both theoretical and experimental, in what might be called "the molecular basis of memory." The spectacular success of recent investigations of the molecular basis of transmission of genetic information has suggested that there may be an analogous molecular mechanism for storing and utilizing experiential information during the life of the individual— that is, that the memory of an experiential event is stored in the nervous system by the formation or alteration of a particular molecule or set of molecules, which may be regarded as a molecular engram or memory trace. Various types of molecules, including DNA, RNA, proteins, and lipids, have been suggested as the actual engram. This article is an attempt to provide a critique, rather than a comprehensive review, of certain theoretical and experimental approaches to this general hypothesis. Since the particular hypothesis that specific changes in neuronal RNA represent the molecular engram of memory has received special attention of late, we consider it in some detail here. Our aim is to use this particular molecular theory to illustrate the problems that are fundamental to all purely molecular theories which fail to consider the cellular environment within which molecules exist.

* Reprinted from *Science,* Vol. 144, April 3, 1964, pp. 26–29. By permission. Copyright © 1964 by the American Association for the Advancement of Science.

RNA and Memory

A large number of experiments have now been performed which support the view that RNA metabolism may be intimately connected with memory storage and learning. Although there is still a definite controversy about some of the methods and techniques that have been used in these investigations, we limit this discussion to interpretations of experimental data and do not discuss experimental methods. The most direct suggestion that RNA metabolism is involved in memory storage is the report (Hydén and Egyházi, 1962) that a significant change in the base composition of nuclear RNA of Deiters' nerve cells occurs when a rat learns a balancing task (the adenine-to-uracil ratio of the nuclear RNA of these cells was reported to be increased significantly) and that this change persists for at least 48 hours after the end of the learning experiment. Changes in the base composition of RNA in associated glial cells were also reported in these studies (Hydén and Egyházi, 1963).

The formation of an epileptogenic mirror focus, a neurophysiological model of memory, has been shown to be correlated with an increase in the total amount of neuronal RNA in the cells involved (Morrell, 1961). Furthermore, studies on planarians have indicated that ribonuclease blocks the retention of a conditioned response in regenerating planarian tails (Corning and John, 1961), and it has been claimed that learning is transferable from one planarian to another by way of cannibalistic ingestion (McConnell, 1962). However, the interpretation of the cannibalism data is by no means straightforward, since it appears that in these experiments it was transfer of the general capacity to learn, rather than transfer of the specific learning of a particular task, that was being measured. 8-Azaguanine, a purine analog which can cause formation of nonfunctional RNA (Creaser, 1956), has been found to depress a rat's ability to learn a new maze without impairing its ability to traverse and recall a previously well-learned maze (Dingman and Sporn, 1961). This same antimetabolite was also shown to prolong the interval required for "fixation of experience" in an assay in which the spinal cord of rats was used (Chamberlain, Rothschild, and Gerard, 1963); moreover, in the latter report it was noted that 1,1,3-tricyano-2-amino-1-propene, a drug believed to increase the RNA concentration of neurons (Egyházi and Hydén, 1961), shortens the interval required for "fixation of experience." Finally, long-term administration of yeast RNA has been reported to improve memory function in human subjects with cerebral arteriosclerotic and presenile dementia (Cameron and Solyom, 1961); and, in animal experiments, long-term treatment with yeast RNA increased the rate at which the animal acquired a behavioral response motivated by shock (Cook et al., 1963).

Criteria for a Permanent Memory Trace

None of the experiments just described directly tests the proposition that an RNA molecule, or set of molecules, represents the molecular engram which is the permanent memory trace; they merely stress the fact that RNA metabolism is an important parameter of neuronal function. In order to prove that a given molecule or set of molecules may be regarded as a permanent memory trace, a more rigorous set of criteria should be met.

We suggest that the following criteria must be satisfied in order to demonstrate that a given molecule, set of molecules, structure, or set of structures is indeed a permanent memory trace: (1) It must undergo a change of state in response to the experience to be remembered. (2) The altered state must persist as long as the memory can be demonstrated. (3) Specific destruction of the altered state must result in permanent loss of the memory.

If these criteria are applied to the experimental data relating RNA and memory, it is apparent that the evidence that RNA molecules are specific memory traces is highly circumstantial at present. In particular, a change in the base composition of nuclear RNA in cells involved in a learning task does not necessarily signify that these RNA molecules are permanent memory traces; it might signify that they are transient intermediates in the formation of permanent memory traces, or merely that changes in RNA occur concomitantly with learning. The effects of ribonuclease on learning in planarians may also be regarded in this fashion, since this enzyme was applied during the time the "trained" tail was regenerating a head, and presumably, then, during the process of formation of permanent memory traces in the regenerating head. Likewise, in the experiments in which drugs were used to affect RNA metabolism during the fixation of experience, the drugs were active at the time the proper functioning of transient intermediates in the formation of memory traces would be expected to be important.

In summary, not all the experiments cited have yet satisfied criteria 2 and 3 for establishing a set of molecules as a permanent memory trace. Indeed, any attempt to show that specific destruction of a particular set of molecules results in the permanent loss of an already established memory trace would appear to be beset with great experimental difficulties. Thus, in experimental work on the RNA hypothesis, it has not yet been possible to distinguish between the following alternatives:

(1) RNA molecules, like many other types of molecules, are important constituents of the nervous system, whose structural and functional state may change dramatically during a learning experience, but they do not function as permanent memory traces; or

(2) RNA molecules do have a unique role in the nervous system, that of serving as the final engram of experiential memory, the permanent memory trace.

A Restatement of the Problem

It should be apparent that there is now an abundance of data which suggests some relationship between RNA metabolism in brain and the process of memory storage. What, however, is known about the specificity of this relationship? The major function of all known types of RNA is participation in protein synthesis (Watson, 1963); no other function has thus far been demonstrated for RNA in the brain. Since protein synthesis is one of the most fundamental of all cellular processes, and since the proteins of a cell are largely responsible for its behavior, one would expect that the process of memory storage in a neuron might well involve some participation of the protein-synthesizing mechanism (Waelsch and Lajtha, 1961). It is not surprising to find that this mechanism may undergo some change of state during cellular activity, or that interference with this mechanism may cause changes in the overall behavior of a cell. Indeed, it would be more surprising if it could be unequivocally demonstrated that RNA function is in no way involved in memory storage. The important point is that proponents of the RNA hypothesis have yet to demonstrate that a unique set of RNA molecules functions as specific permanent memory traces. Criticisms of the RNA hypothesis similar to this one have also been made by Briggs and Kitto (1962).

At this point one might raise the question: Is there perhaps an inherent difficulty in any hypothesis which attempts to explain the encoding of memory solely in terms of one set of molecules? Cellular metabolism is not merely a rigid hierarchy whereby DNA controls the synthesis of RNA, RNA controls the synthesis of proteins, and proteins control the synthesis of other metabolites in the cell. Rather, the cell has many regulatory mechanisms, whereby proteins, hormones, and metabolites of low molecular weight may regulate the synthesis of RNA by DNA, as well as many feedback mechanisms for the regulation of functional activity of enzymes (Karlson, 1963). Thus, one cannot logically specify one set of molecules as totally controlling the activities of another set. Furthermore, in the neuron, in which certain functional activities (for example, RNA synthesis) are localized in the cell body and other functional activities (for example, synaptic transmission) are localized in peripheral processes of the cell, the cell body and peripheral synaptic structures exert mutual regulatory effects. Consequently, proper functioning of the nucleic-acid- and protein-synthesizing mechanisms of the cell body is necessary for the proper maintenance of synaptic structure (Waelsch and Lajtha, 1961), and the phenomenon of axoplasmic flow would appear to provide the necessary communication channel whereby centrally synthesized metabolites reach the peripheral synaptic regions (Weiss and Hiscoe, 1948). Moreover, proper synaptic function is necessary for the proper performance of the nucleic-acid- and protein-synthesizing structures of the cell body. A great deal of experimental work indicates that pronounced changes in the state of RNA and proteins occur in the cell body of a neuron that is actively stimulated (Hydén, 1960), and, conversely, that removal of afferent stimulation of a neuron can also cause marked changes in its cell body (Mendelson and Ervin, 1962). The latter phenomenon is dramatically illustrated by the extreme degeneration of cell bodies of retinal ganglion cells of rabbits that were born and raised in darkness and never received visual stimulation (Brattgard, 1952). Moreover, there is much evidence, from the neuroembryological literature, which indicates that the nature of efferent connections of neurons may influence the structure and function of the cell body (Weiss, 1955). Whereas we now understand the details of some aspects of the synthetic mechanisms (for example, RNA and protein synthesis) whereby the metabolism of the cell body may control synaptic function, we have almost no understanding of the mechanisms whereby synaptic function may control the metabolism of the cell body.

Thus we may perhaps more adequately investigate the structural basis of the permanent memory trace if we seek to answer the following questions: What permanent changes in neuronal structure and function result from stimulation of the neuron, and what is the mechanism of production of these changes? In such an approach an attempt is made to bridge the gap between current investigations, which emphasize the importance of particular molecules in memory storage, and the more cytologically and physiologically oriented theories of Ramón y Cajal (1910), Hebb (1949), and Sholl (1956), in which emphasis is on the importance of synaptic interrelationships between neurons. These older theories stressed the role of growth of new axonal and dendritic connections as a fundamental process in memory storage and learning. At the time they were formulated, little was known of the molecular biochemistry of nucleic acid and protein sythesis, and thus there is an incompleteness in these formulations. It is now apparent that the molecular and the cytological approaches to the problem of memory are by no means mutually exclusive, especially if one postulates that a major function of the synthetic mechanisms of the cell body is to provide molecules necessary for the growth and maintenance of axonal and dendritic connections. Weiss (1961) has stressed that the adult neuron, as well as the immature neuron, appears to be in a perpetual state of growth or regeneration, or both, and he has emphasized the importance of axoplasmic flow for this process. The axonal termination of a synapse is essentially devoid of ribosomes (Palay, 1956), which are necessary for protein synthesis; hence, any new proteins required for new axonal growth would, presumably, have to be synthesized in the cell body and reach new synapses by the process of axoplasmic flow. The major advantage of including synaptic structure and function in any hypothesis of memory storage is that one thereby takes into consideration a unique cytological feature of the neuron—namely, the fact that such a vast amount of its surface area (Sholl, 1956) and functional mass (Lowry et al., 1954; Freide, 1961) is located a great distance from the central cell body. As Sholl (1956) has noted, "The activity of a single cortical neuron may well affect that of 4000 other neurons, [while] a single neuron may have more than 50 dendritic branches." No other type of cell in the body has thus become specialized for direct intercellular communication. Moreover, consideration of possible changes in synaptic structure during memory storage may provide an experimental approach to test for satisfaction of criteria 2 and 3; hypotheses which consider memory storage solely at the molecular level have been weakest at this point. Therefore, we may be able to achieve a more comprehensive understanding of the phenomenon of memory if we regard this process as a property of a neuron or set of neurons rather than solely as a property of individual molecules. The molecular approach to the problem has already elucidated certain crucial biochemical processes which might underlie this phenomenon, but the picture is by no means complete at present.

Some Future Problems

In biochemical studies of memory, little attention has been paid, so far, to the lipids of the nervous system, in spite of the fact that lipids are such an important constituent of synaptic membranes. Little is known about the turnover of phospholipids and sphingolipids in such cell membranes. Are such lipids synthesized peripherally, or must they, too, reach the synapse by axoplasmic flow after being synthesized in the cell body? Are new membranes formed as part of the establishment of the memory trace? The recent description of specific inhibitors of fatty-acid synthesis (Brady, 1963; Robinson, Brady, and Bradley, 1963) should make possible an experimental approach to some of these problems.

The kinetics of the behavioral effects of drugs which have been used to produce a specific inhibition or acceleration of synthesis of essential metabolites is another problem which has so far received scant attention. If synthesis of certain necessary metabolites for synaptic growth occurs in the cell body, inhibition or acceleration of such synthetic activities may not be immediately reflected at the synapse. The rate of axoplasmic flow has been estimated to be of the order of 1 to several millimeters per day (Droz and Leblond, 1962; Ochs, Dalrymple, and Richards, 1962; Weiss and Hiscoe, 1948); thus, in neurons with long processes, there may be a considerable delay between the time a molecule is synthesized and the time it reaches peripheral regions of the neuron. It is thus suggested that, in studies of the kinetics of memory-trace formation, both the initial learning and the later retention trials should be carried out at varying intervals after administration of drugs whose principal mechanism of action is upon synthetic activities in the cell body, since such drugs may fail to produce an immediate behavioral effect but may have a pronounced delayed effect. Some of these problems have been approached in the recent and intriguing investigations of Flexner et al. (1962, 1963) on the effects of puromycin (an inhibitor of protein synthesis) on learning and memory in mice. These workers investigated the effect of injecting the drug at various sites and the effect of varying the interval between the initial learning experience and the subsequent administration of puromycin, and they found that under certain conditions puromycin caused loss of memory. Further experiments, on the effect of varying the interval between an initial injection of puromycin and a subsequent learning experience, would be of interest in evaluating the hypothesis that axoplasmic transport of newly synthesized proteins to synaptic terminals is necessary for the fixation of new experiences by means of synaptic growth.

The mechanism of synaptic influence on the metabolism of the cell body is yet another major problem to be solved. It has been suggested (Briggs and Kitto, 1962; Krech, Rosenzweig, and Bennett, 1960; Rosenzweig et al., 1962; Smith, 1962) that the phenomenon of enzyme induction brought about by synaptic stimulation may be important in establishing memory traces, but experimental evidence is scanty. The finding of changes in base ratios of RNA in response to learning situations does not prove that there has been induction of a new type of RNA; since there are many types of RNA in the cell, a change in the relative proportions of the different types being synthesized could produce the same result as induction of a new type. Further studies on the specificity of any such evoked changes in the metabolism of the cell body are critically needed.

Summary

If one establishes a rigorous set of criteria for defining a given type of molecule as a memory trace in the nervous system, then no one type of molecule may at present be regarded as the sole engram of a permanent memory trace. Much evidence already exists that RNA and protein metabolism are intimately involved in the process of memory storage, but the role of other molecules, such as lipids, must also be considered. Sophisticated techniques of molecular biology and enzymology will undoubtedly provide valuable data on biochemical processes involved in memory storage. However, a comprehensive theory of the structural basis of memory must also consider the function of the entire neuron, with consequent emphasis on the reciprocal relationships between the cell body and the synapse, as well as the complex functional interrelationships between neurons.

REFERENCES

Brady, R. O. Studies of inhibitors of fatty acid biosynthesis: III. Mechanism of action of tetrolyl-coenzyme A. *Biochim. Biophys. Acta,* 1963, **70,** 467–468.

Brattgard, S. O. The importance of adequate stimulation for the chemical composition of retinal ganglion cells during early post-natal development. *Acta Radiol. Suppl.,* 1952, **96,** 1–80.

Briggs, M. H., and Kitto, G. B. The molecular basis of memory and learning. *Psychol. Rev.,* 1962, **69,** 537–541.

Cameron, D. E., and Solyom, L. Effects of ribonucleic acid on memory. *Geriatrics,* 1961, **16,** 74–81.

Chamberlain, T. J., Rothschild, G. H., and Gerard, R. W. Drugs affecting RNA and learning. *Proc. Natl. Acad. Sci.,* 1963, **49,** 918–924.

Cook, L., Davidson, A. B., Davis, D. J., Green, H., and Fellows, E. J.

Ribonucleic acid: Effect on conditioned behavior in rats. *Science*, 1963, **141**, 268–269.

Corning, W. C., and John, E. R. Effect of ribonuclease on retention of conditioned response in regenerated planarians. *Science*, 1961, **134**, 1363–1365.

Creaser, E. H. The assimilation of amino acids by bacteria: The effect of 8-azaguanine upon enzyme formation in staphylococcus aureus. *Biochem. J.*, 1956, **64**, 539–545.

Dingman, W., and Sporn, M. B. The incorporation of 8-azaguanine into rat brain RNA and its effect on maze learning by the rat: An inquiry into the biochemical basis of memory. *J. Psychiat. Res.*, 1961, **1**, 1–11.

Droz, B., and Leblond, C. P. Migration of proteins along the axons of the sciatic nerve. *Science*, 1962, **137**, 1047–1048.

Egyházi, E., and Hydén, H. Experimentally induced changes in the base composition of the ribonucleic acids of isolated nerve cells and their oligodendroglial cells. *J. biophys. biochem. Cytol.*, 1961, **10**, 403–410.

Flexner, J. B., Flexner, L. B., Stellar, E., de la Haba, G., and Roberts, R. B. Inhibition of protein synthesis in brain and learning and memory following puromycin. *J. Neurochem.*, 1962, **9**, 595–605.

Flexner, J. B., Flexner, L. B., and Stellar, E. Memory in mice as affected by intracerebral puromycin. *Science*, 1963, **141**, 57–59.

Friede, R. L. Thalamocortical relations reflected by local gradations of oxidative enzymes. In S. S. Kety and J. Elkes (Eds.), *Regional neurochemistry*. New York: Pergamon, 1961. Pp. 151–159.

Hebb, D. O. *The organization of behavior*. New York: Wiley, 1949.

Hydén, H. The neuron. In J. Brachet and A. E. Mirsky (Eds.), *The cell*. Vol. 4. New York: Academic Press, 1960. Pp. 215–323.

Hydén, H., and Egyházi, E. Nuclear RNA changes of nerve cells during a learning experiment in rats. *Proc. Natl. Acad. Sci.*, 1962, **48**, 1366–1373.

Hydén, H., and Egyházi, E. Glial RNA changes during a learning experiment in rats. *Proc. Natl. Acad. Sci.*, 1963, **49**, 618–623.

Karlson, P. New concepts on the mode of action of hormones. *Perspect. Biol. Med.*, 1963, **6**, 203–214.

Krech, D., Rosenzweig, M. R., and Bennett, E. L. Effects of environmental complexity and training on brain chemistry. *J. comp. physiol. Psychol.*, 1960, **53**, 509–519.

Lowry, O. H., Roberts, N. R., Leiner, K. Y., Wu, M., Farr, A. L., and Albers, R. W. The quantitative histochemistry of brain: III. Ammon's horn. *J. biol. Chem.*, 1954, **207**, 39–49.

McConnell, J. V. Memory transfer through cannibalism in planarians. *J. Neuropsychiat.*, 1962, **3** (suppl. 1), 542–548.

Mendelson, J. H., and Ervin, F. R. Influences of afferent neurons on efferent neurons: I. Effects of deafferentation on brain function and behavior. In R. G. Grenell (Ed.), *Progress in neurobiology*. Vol. 5. New York: Hoeber, 1962. Pp. 178–210.

Morrell, F. Electrophysiological contributions to the neural basis of learning. *Physiol. Rev.*, 1961, **41**, 443–494.

Ochs, S., Dalrymple, D., and Richards, G. Axoplasmic flow in ventral root nerve fibers of the cat. *Exp. Neurol.*, 1962, **5**, 349–363.

Palay, S. L. Synapses in the central nervous system. *J. biophys. biochem. Cytol.*, 1956, **2** (suppl.), 193–202.

Ramón y Cajal, S. *Histologie du système nerveux de l'homme et des vertebres.* Paris: A. Maloine, 1910.

Robinson, J. D., Brady, R. O., and Bradley, R. M. Biosynthesis of fatty acids: IV. Studies with inhibitors. *J. Lipid Res.*, 1963, **4**, 144–150.

Rosenzweig, M. R., Krech, D., Bennett, E. L., and Diamond, Marian C. Effects of environmental complexity and training on brain chemistry and anatomy: A replication and extension. *J. comp. physiol. Psychol.*, 1962, **55**, 429–437.

Sholl, D. A. *The organization of the cerebral cortex.* London: Methuen, 1956.

Smith, C. E. Is memory a matter of enzyme induction? *Science,* 1962, **138**, 889–890.

Waelsch, H., and Lajtha, A. Protein metabolism in the nervous system. *Physiol. Rev.,* 1961, **41**, 709–736.

Watson, J. D. Involvement of RNA in the synthesis of proteins. *Science,* 1963, **140**, 17–26.

Weiss, P. Nervous system (neurogenesis). In B. H. Willier, P. Weiss, and V. Hamburger (Eds.), *Analysis of development.* Philadelphia: Saunders, 1955. Pp. 346–401.

Weiss, P. The concept of perpetual neuronal growth and proximo-distal substance convection. In S. S. Kety and J. Elkes (Eds.), *Regional neurochemistry.* New York: Pergamon, 1961. Pp. 220–242.

Weiss, P., and Hiscoe, H. B. Experiments on mechanism of nerve growth. *J. exp. Zool.,* 1948, **107**, 315–395.

SUGGESTIONS FOR ADVANCED READING

Beach, F. A., Hebb, D. O., Morgan, C. T., and Nissen, H. D. (Eds.). *The Neuropsychology of Lashley.* New York: McGraw-Hill, 1960.

Delafresnaye, J. F. (Ed.). *Brain mechanisms and learning.* Oxford: Blackwell, 1961.

Galambos, R., and Morgan, C. T. The neural basis of learning. In Field, J. (Ed.), *Handbook of physiology,* Sect. 1, Vol. 3. Washington, D. C.: American Physiological Society, 1960. Pp. 1471–1499.

Schmitt, F. O. (Ed.). *Macromolecular specificity and biological memory.* Cambridge, Mass.: M.I.T. Press, 1962.

Thomas, G. J. Neurophysiology of learning. *Ann. Rev. Psychol.,* 1962, **13**, 71–106.

3

ELECTRICAL
SELF-STIMULATION
OF THE BRAIN

By allowing a laboratory animal to stimulate its own brain electrically, researchers have been able to study various brain areas to learn whether they mediate positive (approach behavior) or negative (avoidance behavior) effects. The recent emphasis on electrical brain stimulation as a motivating force began with the initial finding of James Olds and Peter Milner that rats would bar-press at a high rate in a Skinner box for electrical stimulation to some brain areas and avoid the bar when stimulation was directed to other areas (Positive reinforcement produced by electrical stimulation of septal area and other regions of rat brain, *J. comp. physiol. Psychol.*, 1954, 47, 419–427).

Research using this technique was initially focused on the location of brain areas that mediate "pleasure" and on the development of adequate methods for differentiating positively and negatively reinforcing brain areas. Results of such studies led to attempts to relate "positive" and "negative" brain areas to other motivational systems, such as hunger, thirst, and sex. Further research has advanced the electrical self-stimulation technique from use in the rat to use in human psychiatric patients. The many studies in this area have formed the basis for a theory of behavior based on the balance between positive and negative brain systems.

In the opening selection, psychologist James Olds reviews the background for this area of research and presents some of the early results that he and his colleagues obtained.

PLEASURE CENTERS IN THE BRAIN*

James Olds

The brain has been mapped in various ways by modern physiologists. They have located the sensory and motor systems and the seats of many kinds of behavior—centers where messages of sight, sound, touch and action are received and interpreted. Where, then, dwell the "higher feelings," such as love, fear, pain and pleasure? Up to three years ago the notion that the emotions had specific seats in the brain might have been dismissed as naive—akin perhaps to medieval anatomy or phrenology. But recent research has brought a surprising turn of affairs. The brain does seem to have definite loci of pleasure and pain, and we shall review here the experiments which have led to this conclusion.

The classical mapping exploration of the brain ranged mainly over its broad, fissured roof—the cortex—and there localized the sensory and motor systems and other areas which seemed to control most overt behavior. Other areas of the brain remained mostly unexplored, and comparatively little was known about their functions. Particularly mysterious was the series of structures lying along the mid-line of the brain from the roof down to the spinal cord, structures which include the hypothalamus and parts of the thalamus. It was believed that general functions of the brain might reside in these structures. But they were difficult to investigate, for two reasons. First, the structures were hard to get at. Most of them lie deep in the brain and could not be reached without damaging the brain, whereas the cortex could be explored by electrical stimulators and recording instruments touching the surface. Secondly, there was a lack of psychological tools for measuring the more general responses of an animal. It is easy to test an animal's reaction to stimulation of a motor center in the brain, for it takes the simple form of flexing a muscle; but how is one to measure an animal's feeling of pleasure?

The first difficulty was overcome by the development of an instrument for probing the brain. Basically the instrument is a very fine needle electrode which can be inserted to any point of the brain without damage. In the early experiments the brain of an animal could

* From *Scientific American,* Vol. 195 (4), October 1956, pp. 105–116.
Reprinted with permission. Copyright © 1956 by Scientific American, Inc.
All rights reserved.

be probed only with some of its skull removed and while it was under anesthesia. But W. R. Hess in Zurich developed a method of studying the brain for longer periods and under more normal circumstances. The electrodes were inserted through the skull, fixed in position and left there; after the skin healed over the wound, the animal could be studied in its ordinary activities.

Using the earlier technique, H. W. Magoun and his collaborators at Northwestern University explored the region known as the "reticular system" in the lower part of the mid-brain. They showed that this system controls the sleep and wakefulness of animals. Stimulation of the system produced an "alert" electrical pattern, even from an anesthetized animal, and injury to nerve cells there produced more or less continuous sleep.

Hess, with his new technique, examined the hypothalamus and the region around the septum (the dividing membrane at the mid-line), which lie forward of the reticular system. He found that these parts of the brain play an important part in an animal's automatic protective behavior. In the rear section of the hypothalamus is a system which controls emergency responses that prepare the animal for fight or flight. Another system in the front part of the hypothalamus and in the septal area apparently controls rest, recovery, digestion and elimination. In short, these studies seemed to localize the animal's brain responses in situations provoking fear, rage, escape or certain needs.

There remained an important part of the mid-line region of the brain which had not been explored and whose functions were still almost completely unknown. This area, comprising the upper portion of the middle system, seemed to be connected with smell, and to this day it is called the rhinencephalon, or "smell-brain." But the area appeared to receive messages from many organs of the body, and there were various other reasons to believe it was not concerned exclusively or even primarily with smell. As early as 1937 James W. Papez of Cornell University suggested that the rhinencephalon might control emotional experience and behavior. He based this speculation partly on the observation that rabies, which produces profound emotional upset, seems to attack parts of the rhinencephalon.

Such observations, then, constituted our knowledge of the areas of the brain until recently. Certain areas had been found to be involved in various kinds of emotional behavior, but the evidence was only of a general nature. The prevailing view still held that the basic motivations—pain, pleasure and so on—probably involved excitation or activity of the whole brain.

Investigation of these matters in more detail became possible only after psychologists had developed methods for detecting and measuring positive emotional behavior—pleasure and the satisfaction of specific "wants." It was B. F. Skinner, the Harvard University experimental psychologist, who produced the needed refinement. He worked out a technique for measuring the rewarding effect of a stimulus (or the degree of satisfaction) in terms of the frequency with which an animal would perform an act which led to the reward. For example, the animal was placed in a bare box containing a lever it could manipulate. If it received no reward when it pressed the lever, the animal might perform this act perhaps 5 to 10 times an hour. But if it was rewarded with a pellet of food every time it worked the lever, then its rate of performing the act would rise to 100 or more times per hour. This increase in response frequency from 5 or 10 to 100 per hour provided a measure of the rewarding effect of the food. Other stimuli produce different response rates, and in each case the rise in rate seems to be a quite accurate measure of the reward value of the given stimulus.

With the help of Hess's technique for probing the brain and Skinner's for measuring motivation, we have been engaged in a series of experiments which began three years ago under the guidance of the psychologist D. O. Hebb at McGill University. At the beginning we planned to explore particularly the mid-brain reticular system—the sleep-control area that had been investigated by Magoun.

Just before we began our own work, H. R. Delgado, W. W. Roberts and N. E. Miller at Yale University had undertaken a similar study. They had located an area in the lower part of the mid-line system where stimulation caused the animal to avoid the behavior that provoked the electrical stimulus. We wished to investigate positive as well as negative effects—that is, to learn whether stimulation of some areas might be sought rather than avoided by the animal.

We were not at first concerned to hit very specific points in the brain, and in fact in our early tests the electrodes did not always go to the particular areas in the mid-line system at which they were aimed. Our lack of aim turned out to be a fortunate happening for us. In one animal the electrode missed its target and landed not in the mid-brain reticular system but in a nerve pathway from the rhinencephalon. This led to an unexpected discovery.

In the test experiment we were using, the animal was placed in a large box with corners labeled A, B, C and D. Whenever the animal went to corner A, its brain was given a mild electric shock by the experimenter. When the test was performed on the animal with the electrode in the rhinencephalic nerve, it kept returning to corner A. After several such returns on the first day, it finally went to a different place and fell asleep. The next day, however, it seemed even more interested in corner A.

At this point we assumed that the stimulus must provoke curiosity; we did not yet think of it as a reward. Further experimentation on the same animal soon indicated, to our surprise, that its response to the stimulus was more than curiosity. On the second day, after the animal had acquired the habit of returning to corner A to be stimulated, we began trying to draw it away to corner B, giving it an electric shock whenever it took a step in that direction. Within a matter of five minutes the animal was in corner B. After this, the animal could be directed to almost any spot in the box at the will of the experimenter. Every step in the right direction was paid with a small shock; on arrival at the appointed place the animal received a longer series of shocks.

Next the animal was put on a T-shaped platform and stimulated if it turned right at the crossing of the T but not if it turned left. It soon learned to turn right every time. At this point we reversed the procedure, and the animal had to turn left in order to get a shock. With some guidance from the experimenter it eventually switched from the right to the left. We followed up with a test of the animal's response when it was hungry. Food was withheld for 24 hours. Then the animal was placed in a T, both arms of which were baited with mash. The animal would receive the electric stimulus at a point halfway down the right arm. It learned to go there, and it always stopped at this point, never going on to the food at all!

After confirming this powerful effect of stimulation of brain areas by experiments with a series of animals, we set out to map the places in the brain where such an effect could be obtained. We wanted to measure the strength of the effect in each place. Here Skinner's technique provided the means. By putting the animal in the "do-it-yourself" situation (i.e., pressing a lever to stimulate its own brain), we could translate the animal's strength of "desire" into response frequency, which can be seen and measured.

The first animal in the Skinner box ended all doubts in our minds that electric stimulation applied to some parts of the brain could indeed provide reward for behavior. The test displayed the phenomenon in bold relief where anyone who wanted to look could see it. Left to itself in the apparatus, the animal (after about two to five minutes of learning) stimulated its own brain regularly about once every five seconds, taking a stimulus of a second or so every time. After thirty minutes the experimenter turned off the current, so that the animal's pressing of the lever no longer stimulated the brain. Under these conditions the animal pressed it about seven times and then went to sleep. We found that the test was repeatable as often as we cared to apply it. When the current was turned on and the animal was given one shock as an *hors d'oeuvre,* it would begin stimulating its brain again. When the electricity was turned off, it would try a few times and then go to sleep.

The current used to stimulate was ordinary house current reduced by a small transformer and then regulated between 1 and 5 volts by means of a potentiometer (a radio volume control). As the resistance in the brain was approximately 12,000 ohms, the current ranged from about .000083 to .000420 of an ampere. The shock lasted up to about a second, and the animal had to release the lever and press again to get more.

We now started to localize and quantify the rewarding effect in the brain by planting electrodes in all parts of the brain in large numbers of rats. Each rat had a pair of electrodes consisting of insulated silver wires 0.01 inch in diameter. The two stimulating tips were only about 0.002 inch apart. During a test, the animal was placed in a Skinner box designed to produce a chance-response rate of about 10 to 25 bar-presses per hour. Each animal was given about six hours of testing with the electric current turned on and one hour with the current off. All responses were recorded automatically, and the animal was given a score on the basis of the amount of time it spent stimulating its brain.

When electrodes were implanted in the classical sensory and motor systems, response rates stayed at the chance level of 10 to 25 an hour. In most parts of the mid-line system, the response rates rose to levels of from 200 to 5,000 an hour, definitely indicative of a rewarding effect of the electric stimulus. But in some of the lower parts of the mid-line system there was an opposite effect: the animal would press the lever once and never go back. This indicated a punishing effect in those areas. They appeared to be the same areas where Delgado, Roberts and Miller at Yale also had discovered the avoidance effect —and where Hess and others had found responses of rage and escape.

The animals seemed to experience the strongest reward, or pleasure, from stimulation of areas of the hypothalamus and certain mid-brain nuclei—regions which Hess and others had found to be centers for control of digestive, sexual, excretory and similar processes. Animals with electrodes in these areas would stimulate themselves from 500 to 5,000 times per hour. In the rhinencephalon the effects were milder, producing self-stimulation at rates around 200 times per hour.

Electric stimulation in some of these regions actually appeared to be far more rewarding to the animals than an ordinary satisfier such as food. For example, hungry rats ran faster to reach an electric stimulator than they did to reach food. Indeed, a hungry animal often ignored available food in favor of the pleasure of stimulating itself electrically. Some rats with electrodes in these places stimulated their brains more than 2,000 times per hour for 24 consecutive hours!

Why is the electric stimulation so rewarding? We are currently exploring this question, working on the hypothesis that brain stimulation in these regions must excite some of the nerve cells that would be excited by satisfaction of the basic drives—hunger, sex, thirst and so forth. We have looked to see whether some parts of the "reward system" of the brain are specialized; that is, there may be one part for the hunger drive, another for the sex drive, etc.

In experiments on hunger, we have found that an animal's appetite for electric stimulation in some brain regions increases as hunger increases: the animal will respond much faster when hungry than when full. We are performing similar tests in other places in the brain with variations of thirst and sex hormones. We have already found that there are areas where the rewarding effects of a brain stimulus can be abolished by castration and restored by injections of testosterone.

Our present tentative conclusion is that emotional and motivational mechanisms can indeed be localized in the brain; that certain portions of the brain are sensitive to each of the basic drives. Strong electrical stimulation of these areas seems to be even more satisfying than the usual rewards of food, etc. This finding contradicts the long-held theory that strong excitation in the brain means punishment. In some areas of the brain it means reward.

The main question for future research is to determine how the excited "reward" cells act upon the specific sensory-motor systems to intensify the rewarded behavior.

At the moment, we are using the self-stimulating technique to learn whether drugs will selectively affect the various motivational centers of the brain. We hope, for example, that we may eventually find one drug that will raise or lower thresholds in the hunger system, another for the sex-drive system, and so forth. Such drugs would allow control of psychological disorders caused by surfeits or deficits in motivational conditions.

Enough of the brain-stimulating work has been repeated on monkeys by J. V. Brady and J. C. Lilly to indicate that our general conclusions can very likely be generalized eventually to human beings— with modifications, of course.

In the first article in this section, James Olds provided some basic information about electrical self-stimulation. In the next article he reports findings from his laboratory, where he used the self-stimulation technique to study local effects of hunger, sex, and drugs. These findings help us approach the question: In what ways are positively and negatively reinforcing brain areas related to other motivational systems? They also point out the relevance of such studies for theories of motivation. Because classical drive-reduction theory is inadequate to account for the data presented, a more hedonistic position is suggested by Olds.

SELF-STIMULATION OF THE BRAIN*

James Olds

This article reviews experiments which have led to the discovery and analysis of localized systems in the brain where electric stimulation has positive and negative motivational effects. Basically, the experimental animal in these studies is rewarded or punished by a brain shock. The site of electric stimulation determines the motivational effect.

The studies are important primarily as a beginning step toward filling the large gap which has existed between neurophysiological techniques and an understanding of complex psychological processes. Among other things, they carry the enterprise of brain mapping into the realm of clearly defined motivational functions; this by itself correlates an orderly array of integrative psychological mechanisms with an orderly array of anatomical points in the brain. Furthermore, these studies perform a unification long considered technically impossible between electrophysiological, independent variables and standard, behavioral, dependent variables to produce smooth interaction curves relating the two.

* Reprinted from *Science,* Vol. 127, April 14, 1958, pp. 315–324. By permission. Copyright © 1958 by the American Association for the Advancement of Science.

For psychologists, these experiments help to clarify the basic notions of reward and punishment. Reward and punishment, it is agreed, determine which behaviors will predominate in an organism's repertory and which will be erased from it. Rewarded responses are repeated more frequently than would be expected by chance; punished ones are repeated with less frequency. This is obvious.

Less self-evident is the thesis of the classical theory of reward, according to which reward is interpreted as being the falling phase of the same massive stimulation which at high levels constitutes punishment. This thesis is greatly weakened by the work outlined in this article; however, it has held sway for such a long time in psychology, and it conditions so many basic attitudes, that it will certainly form a foundation stone for the new theories which replace it.

Drive and punishment are synonymous, according to this theory, and a reward is held to be fundamentally nothing more than the reduction of a drive. Physiological conditions which are inimical to survival, such as food deficiencies or tissue damage, cause massive receptor discharge into the central nervous system. This discharge is held to be the drive, and it is held to be reflected in behavioral activation. The latter is a nonselective function of the massive drive stimulation, energizing adaptive and maladaptive responses equally. The drive stimulation, however, also has a selective function by which it combines with other cue stimuli to select those responses which have repaired this particular physiological deficit in the past.

The response actually selected by the combination of drive and cue stimuli is determined entirely by structural cue-response connections whose strength has been determined by prior learning. More specifically, a group of cues actually selects the response which was previously followed by drive reduction in their presence. The drive reduction, on previous occasions, caused a rewarding or positive reinforcing effect which somehow increased the causal connection between these stimuli and this particular response.

The hedonistic view that behavior is pulled forward by pleasure as well as pushed forward by pain is rejected in this classical theory for the more parsimonious notion that pain supplies the push and that learning based on pain reduction supplies the direction.

The work reported in this article clearly shows one implication of the drive-reduction theory to be incorrect, for massive inputs to certain parts of the central nervous system are shown to have rewarding effects. Further, by showing that there are anatomically separate mechanisms for reward and punishment in the brain, it points directly to a physiological basis for the motivational dualism suggested in the hedonistic theory.

In fact, it appears that the area producing rewarding effects, upon electric stimulation, is far larger than the area producing punishment. In one early experiment, 76 electrodes were implanted in the brains of rats in an attempt to get a random sampling of midbrain and forebrain points. It was found that stimulation at 47 of these points had motivational effects. Stimulation of 36 of these motivational points produced approach behavior—that is, the rats stimulated themselves repeatedly by means of the technique described below; at only 11 points did stimulation produce avoidance behavior (Olds, 1956a).

Basic Studies

Method. The method of self-stimulation (Olds and Milner, 1954) is modeled in part after the chronic implantation technique of W. R. Hess (1949) and in part after the box technique of B. F. Skinner (1938). The former developed a technique for implanting electrodes permanently in the brain; the technique allows stimulation in the freely behaving animal. The latter worked out a way to measure positive reinforcement—that is, reward—by arranging a situation in which the experimental animal could deliver the reward to itself by a very simple manipulation, and then counting the frequency of the manipulations. Self-stimulation combines these techniques by allowing animals to deliver shocks to specific points in their brains through chronically implanted electrodes.

When the rat stepped on a pedal, a shock was delivered to its brain. The rat never received any other reward for pressing the pedal, and the shock was never turned on except when the rat turned it on itself by stepping on the pedal.

In this box, animals invariably stepped on the pedal about 25 times during the first hour (although there was no rewarding electrical stimulation at all), because the pedal was so placed that it would be pressed when the animal looked out the only opening in the box. After the first hour there were about 5 responses or less per hour during hours in which no reward was produced. If the pedal-pressing produced a reward, the rate, even for the first hour, rose to 200 or more responses an hour; thus, "reward" was clearly discernible. If the pedal-pressing produced punishment, the rate dropped radically; there were only two or three responses during the total experimental procedure; thus, "punishment" was clearly discernible.

If the electrode was placed in the brain at a point at which maximum self-stimulation is produced, the rat, after its very first electric stimulation, began to search and pursue eagerly. Its response to the first shock was to sniff in all corners of the box and manipulate quickly the objects in its path until it stepped on the pedal a second time. After the rat had pressed the pedal a second or third time, it ceased to wander and began to respond at the rate of one or two pedal-presses per second. These animals learned to press the pedal within a minute or two.

A plastic electrode carrier . . . was screwed to the skull and a pair of silver-wire electrodes implanted in the brain through a hole in the skull. The insulated wires, which were 0.01 inch in diameter, stimulated the brain only at their tips. The electrode apparently fired cells up to a distance of at least 0.5 millimeter from its tip. . . . In these experiments each brain was sectioned and stained after testing; all statements about localization are based on examination of this histological material.

The stimulus was a sine-wave shock at 60 cycles per second; the current ranged from 5 to 100 microamperes; the animal received a shock lasting for a maximum of 0.5 second. If the animal held the pedal down for less than 0.5 second, the current went off when it released the pedal. If it held the pedal down for longer than 0.5 second, the current went off automatically and the rat had to release the pedal and press it again to produce another shock.

Locus. Electric stimulation in most parts of the rhinencephalon, and in many parts of the hypothalamus and related structures, produced the approach response (Olds, 1956a). Stimulation in small areas in the midbrain and in certain adjacent parts of the thalamus and hypothalamus produced the avoidance response. Such avoidance behavior was first demonstrated in the cat, by Delgado, Roberts, and Miller (1954). In the rat, the area in which stimulation produced avoidance behavior was small compared with the area in which it produced approach behavior.

The rate of self-stimulation tended to diminish steadily as the site of stimulation was moved toward the cortex. Rates as high as 7,000 per hour were achieved when electric stimulation was applied in the region of the interpeduncular nucleus of the tegmentum.

With electrodes placed in the posterior hypothalamus, just in front of the mammillary body, very high rates, in the range of 5,000 per hour, occurred frequently. With electrodes placed in the anterior hypothalamus, rates ranged from 400 to 1,100 per hour. With electrodes placed farther forward, in the preoptic and telencephalic areas, there was a second series of rates, ranging from quite high ones (about 3,000 per hour) for the preoptic area to very low ones (about 200 per hour) for the anterior forebrain. The high rates obtained in the forebrain series were lower than the high ones of the hypothalamic series.

Thus, there was, for the hypothalamus, a decline of response rates as the electrode was moved forward. There was a similar trend for the telencephalic region, and the rates for the whole of the telencephalic region seemed to be lower than those for the whole of the hypothalamic region.

Electric Current. Studies in which the level of electric current was varied provide some basis for explaining these differences in rate of self-stimulation. The level of the shock was raised from 0 to 150 microamperes by steps of 10. Self-stimulation rates started at chance levels of about 4 to 40 responses per hour and remained at these chance levels at 0, and sometimes at 10, microamperes. Then, usually at 20 or 30 microamperes, but sometimes at 10 microamperes or less, a threshold was crossed and self-stimulation rates rose rapidly. As the current was raised further, the response rate showed a steady increase, undulated, or showed no further increase.

We assume that the cells and fibers excited by the electric stimulus obey the all-or-none principle and have relatively similar thresholds. If this is true, each increase in current brings cells at a greater radius from the tip of the electrode to threshold.

Thus, the steep asymptotic curves [obtained from anterior forebrain and posterior hypothalamus] indicate that stimulation of several rings of cells around the electrode tip induced the rat to stimulate itself with progressively greater frequency. The undulating curves obtained by stimulation in the middle hypothalamus suggest that stimulation of some rings of cells decreases the rate of self-stimulation; from other evidence it is known (Olds, 1956a) that "negative" or "punishing" areas infiltrate into the "reward" system in the part of the middle hypothalamus from which these curves were obtained. The "square" curves obtained for the dorsal septal area show that only one ring of cells around the electrode tip had any motivational function; the rest were neutral. Such "square" functions have always resulted when the electrodes were implanted in or near the diagonal band of Broca; the threshold increased as the distance of the electrode from the diagonal band increased. These data on electric current level permit an important inference to be drawn: the asymptotic self-stimulation rate of an area probably depends on the number of concentric rings of "reward" cells surrounding the tip of the electrode.

The square curves indicate several other important points. Since the full rate occurred at 10 microamperes, when the electrodes were in the diagonal band, it appears that cells outside the diagonal band are neutral (the diagonal band is, thus, the only active site in the septal area). The fact that current up to 150 microamperes does not slow the rate of self-stimulation indicates that the reward units of the diagonal band are affected equally by any current from 10 microamperes (threshold) to 150 microamperes (15 times threshold). Since this function was produced repeatedly by the same rat every day for 8 months, it may be assumed that the current of 15 times threshold did no damage to the nearby cells which produce self-stimulation.

Finally, because electrodes may be placed at varying distances from the diagonal band, it is possible to define the shape and size of the suprathreshold electric field produced by various levels of electric current.

Summary. (1) The areas in which the stimulation produces the approach or rewarding effect occupy a larger proportion of the brain than do the areas in which the avoidance or punishing effect is produced. Therefore, the brain cannot be thought of as tending mainly to produce behaviors which *decrease* its own excitation, for a large portion causes behaviors which *increase* excitation. (2) There is some sort of orderly arrangement of the rewarding effect in the rhinencephalon and related structures, with the result that response rates tend to decline as stimulation is moved forward toward the cortex; this is true both within structures and from structure to structure. (3) Finally, by gauging the way in which rates of self-stimulation increase as the strength of the brain-shock increases, it is possible to estimate the size of the sphere, surrounding a point of stimulation, in which electric stimulation is rewarding. When the size of this sphere is large, as in the ventral posterior hypothalamus, the rate of self-stimulation at high-current levels is very high. When there is only a narrow ring, as in the dorsal septal area, the rate, even at high-current levels, is low.

Analytic Studies

Further studies indicate that the electrical brain-shock reward has the effect of a strong primary-reward object in several different experimental situations. These studies suggest also that the electric brain shock excites cells which are normally involved in the mediation of the effects of conventional primary reinforcers such as food and sex objects.

Maze Running. At first it seemed possible that the animal did not really seek the electric stimulus but pressed the pedal only as a result of some sort of compulsion in a small, confined box. Maze studies (Olds, 1956b), however, indicated that animals show day-to-day learning of a complex problem in order to get the electric reward. Test animals certainly ran as fast as, if not faster than, others running for a food reward. In the case of a runway instead of a maze (Olds, 1956b), animals ran much faster for the electric stimulus than for food.

Obstruction Box. The next two studies were concerned with the strength and duration of the drive for self-stimulation. To study the strength of the drive, [an] obstruction box . . . was used. In this study, the rat was permitted to stimulate itself three times at one lever. Then it had to cross a grid, which delivered an increasingly painful foot shock, to stimulate itself three more times at the opposite lever. It went back and forth until the foot shock became so great that it stopped the rat from crossing. Healthy, well-fed rats running for a brain-shock reward endured far more painful shock to the feet than did 24-hour-hungry rats running for food. The drive for self-stimulation appeared to be (in some cases) at least twice as strong as a 24-hour hunger drive.

Satiation. As for the endurance of the drive for self-stimulation, two questions may be asked: (1) How many days did the drive last if rats were allowed to stimulate themselves for an hour per day? (2) How many minutes or hours did the drive last if rats were allowed to stimulate themselves continuously?

When animals were run for periods of an hour a day, they usually maintained the same rate of self-stimulation throughout the hour and for as many days or months as they were tested. Such stable rates were obtained when high suprathreshold electric current (60 to 100 microamperes) was used.

If animals with electrodes implanted in the hypothalamus were run for 24 hours or 48 hours consecutively, they continued to respond as long as physiological endurance permitted. Rats with electrodes implanted in the telencephalon, on the other hand, seemed to slow down considerably when they were shifted from a 1- to a 24-hour self-stimulation schedule. . . . Animals with electrodes in the telencephalon appeared to show some genuine satiation. No similar satiation appeared in animals with electrodes in the hypothalamus.

Effects of Drives. Further studies showed that the animal's taste for the electric reward is often sensitive to basic drives in the way that its taste for conventional rewards is. The extensive reward system appears to break down into subsystems subservient to the different basic drives; there appears to be a food-reward system, a sex-reward system, and so on.

If electric stimulation at some points fires cells that mediate food reward, the animal's appetite for self-stimulation at this point may go up and down with hunger as its appetite for food does. A large series of animals has been tested in order to compare their rates of self-stimulation when hungry with their rates when full. When tests were made at a constant current of 65 microamperes with a set of electrodes placed in the midline of the brain, in the ventromedial hypothalamus, and in the septal area, hunger seemed to have an important positive effect, increasing self-stimulation rates (Olds, 1956c, 1961). When, however, animals were tested at *a series of current levels,* a somewhat different picture of the hunger system appeared.

In the latter experiments animals were tested every day at a series of shock levels; accordingly, they yielded a series of response rates (usually of increasing magnitude). Each shock level was maintained for 8 minutes, response output was recorded, and then the shock was shifted to the next higher level. Zero microamperes (no reward) was usually maintained for the first interval, and then the shock level was raised to 5 microamperes, 10 microamperes, and so on. Response rates started at very low (chance) levels during the first interval and gradually rose to an asymptote characteristic of the area of stimulation.

Animals were run alternately—one day hungry and the next day full—to see whether this would change the rate of self-stimulation during the various intervals. Many animals responded faster when hungry and slower when sated, but this difference appeared only at a limited range of electric shock levels. The shock level at which the hunger difference appeared is called the "threshold of the hunger effect."

Before discussing these thresholds, I shall mention the gross findings of this recent hunger study. When electrodes were in the hypothalamus, all large hunger effects on self-stimulation were obtained with those electrodes which were clustered in the posterior sector. No hunger effects were found when electrodes were in the portion of the anterior hypothalamus that was explored. With electrodes in the telencephalon, however, strong hunger effects appeared again in a rather unclear pattern. With electrodes in the posterior hypothalamus, [an] interesting and orderly picture . . . was obtained.

Thresholds for the hunger effect declined as the location of the electrodes approached a point about 1.25 millimeters lateral to the midline at a point just in front of the mammillary body. If we assume that a hunger-reward center is located at this point, we find that it can be reached by 10 microamperes of current from electrodes at points about 0.25 millimeter away and by 20 microamperes from electrodes at points about 0.5 millimeter away. From these data we may surmise that a 50-microampere stimulus has a suprathreshold field with a diameter of about 1 millimeter. . . .

A hunger differential appears, we may surmise, whenever an electric field is increased to the point where there is a hunger-sensitive area on the boundary between the supra- and subthreshold parts. If this is true, our data suggest a sharp localization of a hunger reward center in the hypothalamus and a very compact relation between it and the other drive-reward centers in the hypothalamus—a relation so compact that different effects will be achieved at different current levels.

Androgen-Level Studies

In androgen-level studies, animals were castrated after they had been trained to press the lever for brain shock. After castration, rates of self-stimulation were measured for 14 days of declining androgen level. Then testosterone propionate was injected, in doses of from 1 to 5 milligrams per animal, and rates were measured over a period of days while androgen levels rose and fell again. A series of testosterone injections was also given to see how rates of self-stimulation were maintained under androgen replacement therapy.

Two sets of data [were obtained] from this study. . . . First, with an electrode in the dorsomedial caudate nucleus, an all-or-none relation between rate of response and testosterone level was obtained. The animal was tested each day at a series of levels of current, from 15 to 55 microamperes. The animal responded well for a 15-microampere current when androgen levels were high; it did not respond at all, even for a 55-microampere current, when androgen levels were low. The animal was taken through several androgen cycles. At high levels it always responded; at low levels it did not. At the termination of its career the rat was responding at a very high level, and post-mortem examination showed that its seminal vesicles were not only as large as those of noncastrated rats but, indeed, were larger than normal. Thus, it is possible to get all-or-nothing drive effects from self-stimulation with electrodes in some parts of the caudate nucleus.

The second point is that there is an inverse relation between androgen effects and hunger effects on the rate of self-stimulation. Hunger effects and androgen effects on rate of self-stimulation were measured in 16 animals, with electrodes in different parts of the hypothalamus and telencephalon, on 1-hour self-stimulation runs with a stimulus of 1 volt (about 60 to 80 microamperes). Animals which showed a strong increase in rate of self-stimulation in response to androgen showed a decline in rate of self-stimulation in response to hunger, and vice versa. In other words, if hunger raised the response rate, androgen lowered it; if androgen raised the response rate, hunger lowered it. If we presume that the placement of the electrode determines the degree of sensitivity to hunger or to androgens, this study gives a firm basis for expecting to find anatomical differentiation between the hunger-reward system and the androgen-reward system.

Other experiments showed the effect of forced electric stimulation on food consumption (consummatory behavior). In these experiments, electrodes were implanted and were used first to test the effect of stimulation on food consumption. The animals were maintained on an *ad libitum* diet. Eating, under stimulation, in stimulation boxes, was measured for 1 hour per day with a current of about 80 microamperes applied for 0.5 second every 10 seconds. Other groups were stimulated with a current of 25 microamperes applied for 0.5 second every second. Measures of food intake under stimulation were matched against food intake during control weeks, during which there was no stimulation. As has been reported by others (Delgado and Anand, 1953), stimulation in the ventral posterior hypothalamus at points about 1.5 millimeters lateral to the midline caused an increase in eating; stimulation medial to these points sometimes, but not always, caused a decrease in eating. After these tests were completed, the same animals were subjected to self-stimulation tests with the same levels of current. The lateral electrode placements, in areas where stimulation seemed to increase hunger drive, were the ones that usually produced extremely high rates of self-stimulation. The medial placements, in areas where stimulation seemed to reduce the hunger drive, ordinarily produced much slower rates of self-stimulation.

To avoid the notion that there is a food reward "center" in the posterior hypothalamus, it should be mentioned that a similar relationship between hunger and electric stimulation seems to exist in several more anterior parts of the brain. . . . Electric stimulation at [a rewarding placement in the telencephalon] increased eating behavior by almost 50 per cent, and the animal stimulated itself at a rate of over 1,000 responses per hour with no change in level of current.

There is a superficial anachronism in these data correlating drive increase (measured by eating behavior) and reward (measured by self-stimulation); reward has classically been thought to be correlated with drive reduction. There is, of course, the possibility that some conflicting drive is reduced by the stimulation, thereby permitting the animal to eat. There may also be neighboring drive and reward areas, both activated by the same electric field. However, the correlation of rewarding properties with a stimulus which produces consummatory behavior need not be surprising. If we think, for example, of a stimulus to a sexual consummatory response, we might expect some rewarding properties. Why not expect a similar result in the case of hunger?

Thus, our analysis permits the following generalizations: (1) the electrical reward is effective where more conventional rewards are effective—in a Skinner box, runway, complicated maze, and obstruction box; (2) the reward has the same effect from day to day over long periods of time; (3) with stimulation through electrodes in some brain areas, hunger augments the rate of self-stimulation, and with stimulation through electrodes in other brain areas, androgens augment the rate; (4) the rewarding stimulus often appears to produce a temporary increment in some consummatory behavior.

Drug Studies

The last part of this article deals with more practical considerations. It seems that certain behavior disorders might be benefited if "reward" or "pleasure" systems of the brain could be selectively controlled by use of pharmacological agents. It might be important to control one of the drive-reward systems without affecting the other systems, or to control the forward or cortical reward systems without affecting the posterior, hypothalamic systems.

For these reasons we have hoped to find differential sensitivity of different reward placements to different drugs with known emotional or psychological effects. In recent drug studies, series of levels of current were used, as in the drive studies. Animals were allowed to stimulate themselves for 8 minutes at each level of current, starting at 0 and working up to 40 or 50 microamperes. As was indicated previously, the animals did not respond at 0 and 5 microamperes. At 10, 15, or 20 microamperes, the animals began to respond.

The 8-minute interval in which they began to respond was called the threshold interval. A drug was injected, to become effective at the beginning of the threshold interval (which had been determined by several weeks of previous control testing).

Tranquilizers. . . . Chlorpromazine [was] injected intraperitoneally at 2 milligrams per kilogram. . . . [With] the electrode . . . in the middle hypothalamus, none of the self-stimulating response was eliminated at threshold, only 25 per cent of the response was eliminated at the next level, and 21 per cent was eliminated at the third level, after which all inhibitory effect of chlorpromazine was over, in this case. In [another] case . . . in which the electrode was placed in the ventral posterior hypothalamus, the effect was much more pronounced; self-stimulation [was] totally eliminated in all six of the intervals [up to 55 microamperes].

A map of the effects of chlorpromazine obtained with 31 cases has been made. It shows that the effects of chlorpromazine are strongly inhibitory on self-stimulation when electrodes are placed in the ventral posterior hypothalamus. With electrodes in the middle hypothalamus, there is a somewhat less marked effect, and with electrodes in the anterior hypothalamus, there is very little effect. The effects are small with electrodes in the anterior preoptic region but seem to become quite strong again with electrodes in parts of the septal region.

With electrodes in the posterior hypothalamus and in the anterior hypothalamus, the same drug has strikingly different effects on the rate of self-stimulation. Since the drug does not greatly slow self-stimulation via electrodes implanted in the anterior hypothalamus, there is some assurance that the drug does not impede behavior as such. Since the drug does greatly slow self-stimulation via electrodes implanted in the ventral posterior hypothalamus, there is some assurance that the drug acts selectively, either on this part of the brain or on some of the areas to which it projects, to produce its rewarding effect. Furthermore, it is reasonable to assume that the areas sensitive to the drug are not essential to all rewarding effects, because anterior hypothalamic stimulation has its rewarding effect in spite of the drug.

Psychotomimetics. Another example of a differential drug effect is the interaction of serotonin and lysergic acid diethylamide. Serotonin is supposedly a transmitter substance in the brain, and lysergic acid diethylamide is a psychotomimetic (producing effects somewhat similar to psychotic hallucinations). Studies by other workers

(Woolley, 1955) have suggested that in some cases serotonin might be antagonistic to the effects of lysergic acid diethylamide. When lysergic acid diethylamide was injected intraperitoneally just prior to the threshold interval, there was usually an inhibitory effect on self-stimulation. In most cases the drug was effective in both the first and second intervals after injection. The effect of the drug appeared most dependably in the second 8-minute interval after injection; therefore, we studied the inhibitory effect on self-stimulation in this second interval in further analysis. We found two types of interaction between lysergic acid diethylamide and serotonin. In the first, lysergic acid diethylamide alone had a strong inhibitory effect on self-stimulation; when serotonin was administered half an hour before the lysergic acid diethylamide injection, however, there was no effect of the latter at all. Finally, bromo-lysergic acid diethylamide, which is like lysergic acid diethylamide but is supposed not to cross easily from the blood into the brain, had no inhibitory effect on self-stimulation. In the second case, lysergic acid diethylamide had a strong effect again. This time, however, serotonin did not antagonize the effect, and bromo-lysergic acid diethylamide had the same effect as lysergic acid diethylamide itself.

. . . When electrodes are in certain delimited parts of the hypothalamus and telencephalon, serotonin fails to antagonize the effects of lysergic acid diethylamide, and in these cases bromo-lysergic acid diethylamide has the same effects as lysergic acid diethylamide. With electrodes implanted in other clear-cut regions, serotonin does antagonize the effects of lysergic acid diethylamide, and these are the cases in which bromo-lysergic acid diethylamide has no inhibitory effects on self-stimulation. Here, again, we have evidence of chemical differentiation between different parts of the reward system.

In some earlier tests on chlorpromazine and reserpine, a constant and quite high voltage level was maintained (Olds, Killam, and Bach-y-Rita, 1956). Striking inhibition of response tendencies by reserpine was found when electrodes were implanted in the posterior hypothalamus, but no effects were found when electrodes were in the telencephalic region. Later work with graduated levels of electric current did not show such a sharp differentiation. The inhibitory effects of reserpine on self-stimulation in the hypothalamus do not appear at low voltages but only at very high ones. These data indicate that reserpine may selectively lower seizure thresholds for stimulation via the posterior hypothalamus. Petit mal states, elicited by stimulation at high voltages plus the reserpine, seem to account for the seeming inhibitory effect of reserpine on self-stimulation via the hypothalamus.

Summary

My conclusions are these: (1) The cells which mediate primary rewarding effects are located in a midline system running from the midbrain through the hypothalamus and midline thalamus and into the subcortical and cortical groups of the rhinencephalon. (2) The cell groups which mediate primary rewarding effects are different from those which mediate primary punishing effects. (3) Despite this relative independence, there are, undoubtedly, relationships of mutual inhibition existing between these two systems. Rewards do, among other things, tend to reduce sensitivity to pain, and punishments do tend to reduce rewarding effects. (4) These primary reward systems of the brain are subdivided into specific drive-reward subsystems mediating the specific drives such as hunger and sex. (5) Because there are also subsystems of this set of rewarding structures sensitive to different chemical effect, it is reasonable to hope that eventually it will be possible to control the reward systems pharmacologically in cases where behavior disorders seem to result from deficits or surfeits of positive motivation.

REFERENCES

Delgado, J. M. R., and Anand, B. K.   Increase of food intake induced by electrical stimulation of the lateral hypothalamus.   *Amer. J. Physiol.*, 1953, **172**, 162–168.

Delgado, J. M. R., Roberts, W. W., and Miller, N. E.   Learning motivated by electrical stimulation of brain.   *Amer. J. Physiol.*, 1954, **179**, 587–593.

Hess, W. R.   *Das Zwischenhirn*.   Basel: Schwabe, 1949.

Olds, J.   A preliminary mapping of electrical reinforcing effects in the rat brain.   *J. comp. physiol. Psychol.*, 1956, **49**, 281–285.   (a)

Olds, J.   Runway and maze behavior controlled by basomedial forebrain stimulation in the rat.   *J. comp. physiol. Psychol.*, 1956, **49**, 507–512. (b)

Olds, J.   Neurophysiology of drive.   *Psychiat. Res. Rep.*, 1956, **6**, 15–20. (c)

Olds, J.   Differential effects of drives and drugs on self-stimulation at different brain sites.   In D. E. Sheer (Ed.), *Electrical stimulation of the brain*.   Austin: Univ. of Texas Press, 1961. Pp. 350–366.

Olds, J., Killam, K. F., and Bach-y-Rita, P.   Self-stimulation of the brain used as a screening method for tranquillizing drugs.   *Science*, 1956, **124**, 265–266.

Olds, J., and Milner, P.   Positive reinforcement produced by electrical stimulation of septal area and other regions of rat brain.   *J. comp. physiol. Psychol.*, 1954, **47**, 419–427.

Skinner, B. F. *The behavior of organisms.* New York: Appleton-Century, 1938.
Woolley, D. W.   Production of abnormal (psychotic?) behavior in mice with lysergic acid diethylamide, and its partial prevention with cholinergic drugs and serotonin.   *Proc. Nat. Acad. Sci.,* 1955, **41**, 338–344.

Most research on electrical self-stimulation of the brain has regarded "reward" operationally as continued bar-pressing for stimulation. Degrees of reward have been considered in terms of rates of bar-pressing for stimulation. But is this method the most adequate for making such evaluations? Psychologists William Hodos and Elliot S. Valenstein think it is not, and in the research described in the following paper they present evidence supporting another method to measure degrees of reward. Their report also points out that conclusions drawn from research results are, to a great extent, a function of the methods used in carrying out the research.

AN EVALUATION OF RESPONSE RATE AS A MEASURE OF REWARDING INTRACRANIAL STIMULATION*

William Hodos and Elliot S. Valenstein

Following the report (Olds and Milner, 1954) that electrical stimulation of certain brain areas can serve as an effective reward, a number of measures have been utilized to assess the relative rewarding effects of stimulation of different brain sites. Early studies (Olds, 1955, 1956) which mapped rewarding brain areas employed measures based on percentage of total time spent responding. This measure was computed by subtracting each 30-second period in which no response was made from the total session duration and converting the remainder into a percentage of the total time. Variations on this time measure have been used by other workers (Delgado and Bursten, 1956). While such measures are sensitive to intervals in which no responses are made, they are quite insensitive to differential behavior during the periods of responding.

* Reprinted from the *Journal of Comparative and Physiological Psychology,* Vol. 55, 1962, pp. 80–84. By permission. Copyright © 1962 by the American Psychological Association.

Later studies presented data based on rate of responding (Brady et al., 1957; Olds, 1958a, 1958b, 1958c; Reynolds, 1958; Sidman et al., 1955). While rate of responding in some respects represents an improvement over earlier measures, it is not entirely satisfactory as an index of the relative rewarding properties of intracranial stimulation (ICS). The limitations of a rate measure can be illustrated by a description of the characteristic response patterns associated with stimulation of various rewarding brain loci. Response rates for posterior hypothalamic stimulation are almost invariably high and uniform. This contrasts sharply with the lower, more irregular rate commonly observed with septal stimulation. Direct observation of animals engaged in self-stimulation behavior reveals that posterior hypothalamic stimulation is accompanied by a stereotyped motor response which usually consists of a backward movement of the head and upper part of the body. After several training sessions these motor effects no longer interfere with responding. With high stimulus intensities, however, animals may be forced back some distance from the lever, resulting in a delay before the next response can be made.

With septal stimulation, animals are typically observed to pause following ICS. During this pause the animal remains motionless for as long as several seconds before returning to the lever. Frequently the animal may exhibit a burst of 3 or 4 responses which are then followed by a longer pause. At high stimulus intensities a burst of rapid responses may be followed by a tonic-clonic seizure, and several minutes may elapse before the animal resumes responding.

An examination of the functional relationship between the intensity of the electrical stimulus and the rate of self-stimulation demonstrates that response rate frequently declines at the higher ICS intensities. Reynolds (1958) and Olds (1958c) have shown that the rate-intensity function appears to have a peak with response rate decreasing above an "optimal" intensity level. At high ICS intensities, depending upon electrode placement, a variety of forced movements, tremors, and seizures disrupt what might otherwise be a smooth and rapid performance.

In view of these differences in response characteristics, it would appear that rate does not accurately reflect the strength of ICS reward. The present report describes an experiment in which the relative rewarding effects of brain stimulation were evaluated by measuring the animal's preferences for one ICS over another. This measure appears to be relatively free from the influences of the disruptive side effects of brain stimulation.

Method

Subjects. The Ss were three adult male albino rats from the colony of the Walter Reed Army Institute of Research.

Electrodes and ICS Parameters. Each animal had a bipolar electrode implanted stereotaxically in the septal area and a second bipolar electrode in the posterior hypothalamus. The electrodes were constructed from .010 inch stainless-steel wire insulated except for the cross section at the tip. A detailed description of the electrodes and the method of implantation are reported elsewhere (Valenstein et al., 1961).

The ICS was a 0.5 second train of biphasic square pulses. Each pulse had a duration of 0.2 millisecond and an interpulse interval of 0.2 millisecond. The frequency of the pulse pairs in the train was 100 per second. ICS intensity ranged from 50 microamperes to 2.5 milliamperes.

Apparatus. The apparatus consisted of a modified Skinner box fitted with two levers separated by a 4-inch-high partition. Pressing either lever resulted in an ICS. The animal had free access to either lever, but simultaneous pressing of both levers was prevented by the partition. The programing of the test sessions was controlled by an automatic system of relay-operated switching circuits, and responses of the animals on each lever were registered on cumulative recorders and digital counters.

Procedure. Each animal was first trained to receive ICS reward from either lever. Later, sampling of both levers by the rat was encouraged by rewarding responses on one lever with a moderate intensity ICS and responses on the other lever with an ICS at the lowest intensity which would still maintain responding. The rats quickly learned to sample both levers before responding continuously for the preferred ICS reward. Following this preliminary training, formal preference testing was initiated. Each animal was given a series of 2-minute tests of preference for different ICS intensities and electrode sites. Between the 2-minute tests the lights in the testing chamber were turned off for a variable period ranging from 10 to 60 seconds. During this time-out period lever presses were not rewarded.

In order to assure the measurement of an actual preference between ICS rewards, absolute judgments on the part of the animals were excluded from the data. This was accomplished by not including in the data any 2-minute test period in which the animal failed to sample both levers during the first 30 seconds of the test period. The number of such exclusions was relatively few.

Experiment 1. Experiment 1 was designed to study preferences between septal and posterior hypothalamic stimulation at different ICS intensities. Two levels of ICS intensity were selected for both septal and posterior hypothalamic stimulation. Low intensity was a value slightly above that required to maintain self-stimulation behavior. Medium intensity was a value 2 to 3 times higher than low intensity.

Each animal was allowed to choose between: (a) low septal and low hypothalamic ICS, (b) low septal and medium hypothalamic ICS, (c) medium septal and a low hypothalamic ICS, and (d) medium septal and medium hypothalamic ICS. A test session consisted of a series of 20, 2-minute tests, so that each of the 4 possible ICS comparisons was presented 5 times. After each 2-minute test the relationship between the levers and the ICS rewards was changed according to a random sequence. The experiment was conducted over a 5-day period so that each ICS comparison was made a total of 25 times.

Prior to and after Experiment 1, the response rates for all ICS intensities and electrode placements were each measured during five 2-minute test sessions.

Experiment 2. Experiment 2 was designed to study preferences for different ICS intensities within a single electrode site. Three levels of ICS intensity were selected. As in Experiment 1, low intensity was a value slightly above the response-maintenance thresholds, and medium intensity was a value 2 to 3 times that of low intensity. High intensity, the third level selected, was 2 to 3 times the value of medium intensity.

Each animal was allowed to choose between ICS of: (a) a low and a medium intensity, (b) a low and a high intensity, and (c) a medium and a high intensity. As in the previous experiment, the 2-minute tests were presented in a random sequence over a 5-day period so that each comparison between ICS intensities was made a total of 25 times.

One septal-electrode rat and one posterior-hypothalamic-electrode rat were chosen for study in this experiment, because the rate-intensity functions obtained from these animals clearly showed a marked decrement in rate at the high intensity of ICS. Before and after Experiment 2, rate-intensity functions were obtained as in Experiment 1.

At the termination of the experiment, the animals were sacrificed, perfused, and their brains fixed in formalin. Frozen sections of the brains were stained with cresylecht violet and the locus of the electrode tip determined.

Results

Figure 1 summarizes the results of the first experiment, in which preferences were obtained between septal and hypothalamic ICS. The data from the three animals are presented separately, but the results are very similar. It can be seen from the lower half of the figure that in each animal the response rate for the hypothalamic ICS is clearly higher than that for the septal ICS. While the data of the preference tests in the upper half of the figure indicate that the hypothalamic stimulation is preferred to septal stimulation in 3 out of the 4 comparisons, a medium septal intensity was consistently preferred to a low hypothalamic intensity. These results were obtained with all three animals but are perhaps most striking in the record of Rat 84. This animal responded three times as rapidly for low hypothalamic as for medium septal stimulation, but in twenty-five 2-minute preference tests, almost 80 per cent of the responses were made on the lever which provided septal stimulation.

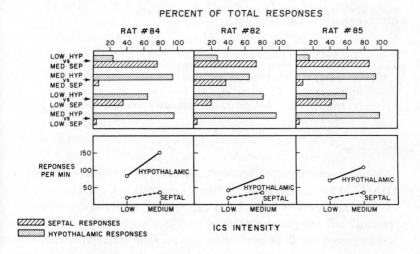

Figure 1. *The upper half of the figure presents the results of preference tests between septal and posterior hypothalamic ICS. The lower half of the figure presents response rates for each ICS intensity and electrode placement.*

In Figure 2 the results of the comparisons between different ICS intensities at the same site of stimulation are summarized. With both septal and hypothalamic ICS the response rate for high-intensity ICS is lower than the rate with medium-intensity stimulation; however, the data clearly demonstrate a preference for the higher intensity. The results are almost identical for both animals. . . .

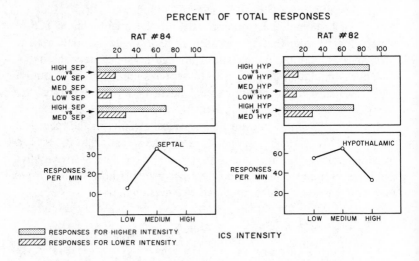

Figure 2. *The upper half of the figure presents the results of preference tests between different ICS intensities within the septal area and posterior hypothalamus. The lower half of the figure presents response rates for each ICS intensity and electrode placement.*

Discussion

In a recent review of his work on self-stimulation of the brain, Olds (1958c) concludes that "the asymptotic self-stimulation rate of an area probably depends on the number of concentric rings of 'reward' cells surrounding the tip of the electrode" (p. 318). Inferences such as these rest upon the implicit assumption that the principal determiner of the rate of intracranial self-stimulation is the relative reward value of the ICS. The present investigation has shown that there are factors, other than the relative reward value of the ICS, which exert a powerful influence on the rate of self-stimulation. In all cases, the animals showed a clear preference for a medium-intensity septal ICS over a low-intensity hypothalamic ICS, in spite of the fact that the response rate was markedly higher with the hypothalamic stimulation. Likewise, when preference tests were made between different intensities of ICS within the septal area or within the posterior hypothalamus, the animals consistently chose the higher intensity, even in instances in which the response rate was lower. As in Experiment 1, the data indicate that one cannot predict relative reward values solely from rate of responding.

Within a given electrode placement, rate appears to correlate well with reward value up to the "optimal" level. At the higher stimulus intensities, responses are disrupted by the motor effects of stimulation and rate is no longer a good index of strength of reward. Moreover, when comparing different brain sites, response characteristics may be so different that reliance on rate may prove to be very misleading.

It is possible that if the effect of the disruptive influences on rate were minimized, rate might then more accurately reflect reward value. In almost all self-stimulation experiments, ICS has followed each response of the animal. However, it has been shown (Brodie et al., 1960; Hodos and Valenstein, 1960; Sidman et al., 1955) that self-stimulation behavior can be maintained with intermittent reward. With schedules which do not employ continuous reward, rate may prove to be a reliable index of reward strength. This, of course, is a question which can be answered experimentally.

In conclusion, it is evident from the data reported above that rate and other time-dependent measures of performance do not give an accurate picture of the relative rewarding properties of different ICS rewards. One cannot infer solely on a basis of a difference in self-stimulation rate that ICS in one neural area is more rewarding than ICS in another. "Maps" of reward gradients throughout the brain should be prepared from the data of direct preference tests or other time-independent measures of relative reward value rather than from the rate of self-stimulation.

Summary

Three male albino rats were implanted with chronic bipolar electrodes in the septal and posterior hypothalamic areas. The rats were trained to press one of two levers; pressing one lever resulted in intracranial stimulation (ICS) through the septal electrode, and pressing the other resulted in ICS through the hypothalamic electrode. Several levels of ICS intensity were used. The animals were allowed to sample both levers and to choose the neural area and ICS intensity which they preferred. Independent measures of response rate at each stimulus intensity and for each electrode placement were obtained. The animals' preferences clearly indicated that rate alone is not an accurate index of relative reward value.

A second experiment studied preferences for different ICS intensities within a single electrode site. Within both the septal area and the posterior hypothalamus, a higher ICS intensity was always preferred to a lower, even in those instances in which the rate of self-stimulation at the higher intensity was less than the rate of self-stimulation at the lower intensity.

The authors conclude that "maps" of reward gradients throughout the brain cannot be based solely on relative rates of self-stimulation.

REFERENCES

Brady, J. V., Boren, J. J., Conrad, D. G., and Sidman, M.   The effect of food and water deprivation upon intracranial self-stimulation.   *J. comp. physiol. Psychol.*, 1957, **50**, 134–137.

Brodie, D., Moreno, O., Malis, J., and Boren, J. J.   Rewarding properties of intracranial stimulation.   *Science,* 1960, **131**, 929–930.

Delgado, J. M. R., and Bursten, B.   Attraction and avoidance evoked by septal rhinencephalic stimulation in the monkey.   *Feder. Proc.,* 1956, **15**, 143. (abstract)

Hodos, W., and Valenstein, E. S.   Motivational variables affecting the rate of behavior maintained by intracranial stimulation.   *J. comp. physiol. Psychol.,* 1960, **53**, 502–508.

Olds, J.   Physiological mechanisms of reward.   In M. R. Jones (Ed.), *Nebraska symposium on motivation: 1955.*   Lincoln: Univ. of Nebraska Press, 1955. Pp. 73–139.

Olds, J.   A preliminary mapping of electrical reinforcing effects in the rat brain.   *J. comp. physiol. Psychol.,* 1956, **49**, 281–285.

Olds, J.   Effects of hunger and male sex hormone on self-stimulation of the brain.   *J. comp. physiol. Psychol.,* 1958, **51**, 320–324.   (a)

Olds, J.   Self-stimulation experiments and differential reward systems. In H. H. Jasper, L. D. Proctor, R. S. Knighton, W. C. Noshay, and R. T. Costello (Eds.), *Reticular formation of the brain.*   Boston: Little, Brown, 1958. Pp. 671–688.   (b)

Olds, J.   Self-stimulation of the brain.   *Science,* 1958, **127**, 315–324. (c)

Olds, J., and Milner, P.   Positive reinforcement produced by electrical stimulation of septal area and other regions of the rat brain.   *J. comp. physiol. Psychol.,* 1954, **47**, 419–427.

Reynolds, R. W.   The relationship between stimulation voltage and rate of hypothalamic self-stimulation in the rat.   *J. comp. physiol. Psychol.,* 1958, **51**, 193–198.

Sidman, M., Brady, J. V., Boren, J., Conrad, D. G., and Schulman, A. Reward schedules and behavior maintained by intracranial self-stimulation. *Science*, 1955, **122**, 830–831.

Valenstein, E. S., Hodos, W., and Stein, L. A simplified electrode assembly for implantation of chronic brain electrodes in small animals. *Amer. J. Psychol.*, 1961, **74**, 125–128.

The reports from Olds's laboratory demonstrated that particular brain areas do mediate pleasure and that the self-stimulation rates obtained from some areas are directly related to hunger and androgen levels. The methodological issues raised by Hodos and Valenstein, though important, do not detract from the findings of Olds and his colleagues.

Results obtained from laboratory rats are important, but are they directly applicable to the study of humans? For ethical and practical reasons, research on electrical self-stimulation of the brain in humans has not matched the extent of such work with lower mammals. The available research, however, does indicate a positive answer to this question. Psychiatrist Robert G. Heath and his colleagues, psychologists M. P. Bishop and S. Thomas Elder, have been at the forefront of this research. Their report on a single patient provides a start toward an answer regarding depth-electrode research in humans. But, as they point out, "any firm conclusions must await the collection of additional data."

INTRACRANIAL SELF-STIMULATION IN MAN*

M. P. Bishop, S. Thomas Elder, and Robert G. Heath

Olds and Milner (1954) first demonstrated . . . that rats will press a lever in order to obtain brief electrical stimulation to various subcortical regions via permanently implanted electrodes. Subsequently, this finding has been replicated many times in rats, and the species generality of the phenomenon has been extended in controlled studies to include the goldfish, guinea pig, bottlenose dolphin, cat, dog, goat, and monkey. These and other data relating to the reinforcing properties of electrical stimulation to certain brain areas have been comprehensively reviewed in a recent article by Olds (1962).

* Reprinted from *Science*, Vol. 140, April 26, 1963, pp. 394–396. By permission. Copyright © 1963 by the American Association for the Advancement of Science. Two figures have been omitted.

Since Heath's initial observations (1954), several reports have appeared describing subjective experiences of an apparently pleasurable nature accompanying electrical stimulation of deep structures in the human brain (Delgado and Hamlin, 1960; Higgens et al., 1956; Sem-Jacobsen, 1959; Sem-Jacobsen and Torkildsen, 1960). Only two previous attempts have been made, however, to employ intracranial self-stimulation (ICSS) techniques with human subjects. Sem-Jacobsen and Torkildsen (1960) report that patients have stimulated their own brains by means of a button switch wired into the stimulation circuit, and Heath (1964), prior to this research, equipped a patient with a small, portable self-stimulator with three buttons which permitted delivery of electrical stimuli of fixed parameters to any of three subcortical sites.

The present study represents an exploratory attempt to investigate human ICSS behavior under strict laboratory conditions such as have been characteristically employed in animal studies. A full report of results to date is in preparation. The present report summarizes some of the major findings.

In the series of depth electrode studies at Tulane (Heath, 1954, 1962a, 1962b; Heath and Mickle, 1960), the primary motivation has always been therapeutic. Only patients who have failed to respond satisfactorily to existing therapies have been studied and treated with these techniques. Electroencephalographic recordings from depth electrodes permit more exact localization of disordered function. More information thus becomes available concerning the nature of the disease processes under study, and more precision is possible when intervention, surgical or other, is indicated, as, for example, in epilepsy and other neurological disorders. With schizophrenic patients, focal electrical stimulation to selected subcortical sites has been shown to produce at least temporary therapeutic benefit (Heath, 1954; Heath and Mickle, 1960; Sem-Jacobsen and Torkildsen, 1960) and, in the Tulane studies, stimulation of activating and "pleasure-inducing" regions has particularly benefited retarded, anhedonic, chronic schizophrenic patients. A vast number of animal ICSS data attest to the powerful reinforcing properties of intracranial stimulation and its consequent efficacy in the modification of behavior (Olds, 1962). Moreover, some of these data (e.g., Olds, 1961; Stein, 1961) implicate abnormal functioning of brain "reward systems" as a primary factor in certain mental disorders, demonstrate the unique value of ICSS techniques in elucidating central effects of psychoactive drugs, and promise eventual pharmacological control of reward-system function in man. The potential usefulness of ICSS procedures in the study and treatment of disordered human behavior is readily apparent. The present research was designed to explore ICSS techniques and to provide preliminary data on effective stimulus parameters and brain "reward" areas in man.

Findings presented here were obtained from a chronic catatonic schizophrenic patient (No. B-12) with multiple depth electrodes in place for 4 months prior to this study. Implanted electrodes were of two types: the "regular" single silver ball (Heath and Mickle, 1960), and a stainless steel array providing multiple contact points. A roentgenographic, stereotaxic technique was employed for accurate implantation and subsequent maintenance of the electrodes (Becker et al., 1957). Patient B-12 is a 35-year-old male with a history of schizophrenia since childhood who has been continuously hospitalized without improvement for the past 9 years. Among other symptoms, he displays a marked tendency toward perseverative behavior which limits ICSS techniques suitable for use with him.

During experimental sessions the subject was seated alone in a soundproof room with a large lever and a hand button available to him. All stimulation, recording, and control apparatus was housed in an adjoining room from which the subject could be observed through a one-way-vision window. Communication with the subject was by means of an intercom system. For all work reported here, the stimulating wave form was a monophasic rectangular pulse of 0.2 millisecond duration, delivered at 100 pulses per second for a fixed stimulus train of 0.5 second. Stimulation was provided by a Grass S-4 stimulator through a stimulus isolation unit and stimulus monitoring device to the subject. Unless otherwise specified, stimulation was bipolar between electrodes 4 mm. apart. The lever and hand button allowed the subject to stimulate his own brain. Functioning of these switches, however, could be controlled by the experimenters to provide current with one device and not the other, or currents of different intensity with the two devices. No visual or auditory cues which might signify such changes were available to the subject.

In our earliest work with a single lever it was noted that while the subject would lever-press at a steady rate for stimulation to various brain sites, the current could be turned off entirely and he would continue lever-pressing at the same rate (for as many as 2,000 responses) until told to stop. Such data obviously justified no conclusions as to reinforcing or "rewarding" properties of the stimulation, but did underscore the need for stringent controls in brain stimulation work with human subjects. Three additional techniques have produced reliable evidence of reinforcing effects of ICSS in man. We have called these the *three current levels, free choice,* and *forced choice* procedures.

The *three current levels* method utilized a single lever. Subject was instructed to respond to a tone signal by pressing the lever (self-stimulating). If he felt nothing or if the stimulus felt neither "good" nor "bad," he was to press 3 times; if it felt "bad," he was to press less than 3 times; if it felt "good," he was to press repeatedly as long as he wished or until told to stop (arbitrarily after 10 responses). After extensive exploration of a given electrode site for preliminary determination of rewarding and aversive current levels, an experimental series was conducted as follows: prior to each tone cue, the current was set at one of three predetermined levels, namely, zero current, the "rewarding" level, or the "aversive" level. Presentation of these currents was on a random basis for a total of 60 trials, 20 at each current level. The number of responses served as the criterion measure.

With this technique, clear evidence of rewarding and aversive properties of intracranial stimulation at varying intensities of current was obtained for the caudate nucleus, amygdala, intralaminar thalamic nuclei, and middle hypothalamus. Rewarding effects in the absence of a higher aversive level were found for the electrode pair tested in the septal area.

It should be noted that the terms "rewarding" and "aversive" as used in this report bear no necessary relation to the patient's subjective response to stimulation. Rather, they are defined operationally by the preferential lever-pressing behavior of the subject.

The free choice and forced choice methods were employed as an independent check on the above findings and for the testing of additional brain sites. With these techniques both the lever and hand button were used. In the *free choice* procedure, the subject was told that he might shift at will from the lever to the button or vice versa. A rewarding current was made available with one of these devices and either an aversive current or zero current with the other. In the course of the subject's responding, these current conditions were reversed by the experimenters so that the current previously available on the lever was now on the button, and vice versa. In addition, the current was sometimes switched off entirely. Because of the subject's marked tendency to respond perseveratively for zero current, most attempts to control his behavior under conditions of rewarding current versus no current were unsuccessful. . . .

The subject initially stayed with the lever which was delivering reward current [0.4 milliamps, to the amygdala] except for seven brief shifts to the aversive button [0.8 milliamps] and back. When the current was turned off, however, he continued as before to respond at the same rate. With the original conditions reversed, he quickly switched to the button, and when they were again reversed, he again responded appropriately. . . . For the reward current versus zero current, again, responding was appropiate. It is of interest that the introduction of an attractive tray of food produced no break in responding, although the subject had been without food for 7 hours, was noted to glance repeatedly at the tray, and later indicated that he knew he could have stopped to eat if he wished. Even under these conditions he continued to respond without change in rate after the current was turned off, until finally instructed to stop, at which point he ate heartily.

The *forced choice* technique was introduced to circumvent the difficulties arising from the subject's tendency to respond perseveratively for no current under free choice conditions. Instructions for this procedure were as before except that in addition to shifting at will from one device to the other, *S* was told that whenever a tone signal was sounded, he was to shift immediately to the other device and that he might then either stay with that one or return to the one he had been pressing, whichever he wished. In short, he was forced with each tone signal to "try out" the other device and decide which he preferred to use. In this procedure a rewarding current was made available on one device and zero current on the other. In conjunction with some tone signals the rewarding current would be shifted by the experimenters to the other device; at other times the tone would be given without such a change being made. . . . Forced choice performance with self-stimulation of the septal area at a current level of 5 milliamps versus no current [shows that] both spontaneous shifts and forced shifts were followed by rapid return to the initially rewarding lever, and when the tone was associated with shift of reward, the subject's preference shifted accordingly. These data appear to provide sound evidence of the reinforcing or rewarding properties of electrical stimulation at this site. Again, however, when the current was turned off entirely, this subject vacillated back and forth a few times and then continued to press the lever without reinforcement for more than half an hour until stopped. This has been a consistent finding with this patient in all work with him to date.

Table 1 summarizes preliminary findings with respect to rewarding and aversive current levels in various subcortical structures. This material is based on data obtained through use of the three techniques

Table 1. *Comparative current intensities, in milli-amperes, for "reward" and "aversive" ICSS respond-ing with various subcortical placements: subject D.S. (No. B-12).*

Structure	"Rewarding"	"Aversive"
Caudate (head)	8.0	10.0
Septal area	3.5 and up	‡
Amygdala	0.4	0.8
Central median thalamus	1.25	2.5
Mid-hypothalamus	0.2	0.4
Posterior hypothalamus	0.5	0.7
Post. hypothalamus-teg-mentum	0.5	0.7
Tegmentum	†	0.2

* Stimulus parameters: unidirectional rectangular pulses of 0.2 msec. dura-tion delivered at 100 pulse/sec. Train duration: 0.5 sec. Bipolar stimulation between electrodes 4 mm. apart in all areas except caudate nucleus (mono-polar) and posterior hypothalamus-tegmentum (electrodes 2 mm. apart).

† Not tested below 0.2 ma. (apparatus limitations).

‡ Stimulation apparently rewarding and nonaversive up to 12.5 ma. Not tested above this level.

described. The current levels specified should not be taken as firmly established even for this subject. They are intended rather to give a general picture of differential thresholds in the various brain areas. Brady (1961) has shown that prior stimulation in one area can affect response rate, and presumably reward threshold, in a second area. In our exploratory work we have not adequately controlled for this variable. Also, there has been indication that sites only a few milli-meters apart in the same structure may show significantly different thresholds. It would appear, however, that current requirements for both rewarding and aversive effects are generally much higher in the forebrain structures than in the hypothalamic-tegmental area. Current requirements indicated for the head of the caudate raise some ques-tion as to whether the rewarding and aversive properties in this case might have resulted from spread of the field of excitation to other structures.

The rather consistent finding of an aversive current level in the range of 25 to 100 per cent above the reward level in a given brain site does not correlate well with most animal data. Olds (1958, 1962) re-ports similar "ambivalent" effects in rats, but these have been less widespread in terms of anatomical locus. Further research is needed to determine whether the present findings may be generalized to other human subjects.

In summary, specialized intracranial self-stimulation techniques have produced data suggestive of the presence of subcortical areas in the human brain in which brief electrical stimulation appears to have rewarding or reinforcing properties. Brain areas thus far suggested as possessing such properties are the head of the caudate nucleus, the septal area, the amygdala, the intralaminar nuclei of the thalamus, the mid-hypothalamus, the posterior hypothalamus, and the boundary of the hypothalamus-tegmentum. With our electrode placements and stimulus parameters, relatively small increases in current above the rewarding level typically produced an aversive effect. These findings are based on data obtained from one clearly nonnormal subject. Any firm conclusions must await the collection of additional data.

REFERENCES

Becker, H. C., Founds, W. L., Peacock, S. M., Heath, R. G., Llewellyn, R. C., and Mickle, W. A. A roentgenographic stereotaxic technique for implanting and maintaining electrodes in the brain of man. *Electroencephal. clin. Neurophysiol.*, 1957, **9**, 533–543.

Brady, J. V. Motivational-emotional factors and intracranial self-stimulation. In D. E. Sheer (Ed.), *Electrical stimulation of the brain*. Austin: Univ. of Texas Press, 1961. Pp. 413–430.

Delgado, J. M. R., and Hamlin, H. Spontaneous and evoked electrical seizures in animals and in humans. In E. R. Ramey and D. S. O'Doherty (Eds.), *Electrical studies on the unanesthetized brain*. New York: Hoeber, 1960. Pp. 133–152.

Heath, R. G. (Ed.). *Studies in schizophrenia*. Cambridge: Harvard Univ. Press, 1954.

Heath, R. G. Brain centers and control of behavior—Man. In J. H. Nodine and J. H. Moyer (Eds.), *Psychosomatic medicine*. Philadelphia: Lea and Febiger, 1962. Pp. 228–240. (a)

Heath, R. G. Common characteristics of epilepsy and schizophrenia: Clinical observation and depth electrode studies. *Amer. J. Psychiat.*, 1962, **118**, 1013–1026. (b)

Heath, R. G. (Ed.). *The role of pleasure in behavior*. New York: Hoeber, 1964.

Heath, R. G., and Mickle, W. A. Evaluation of seven years' experience with depth electrode studies in human patients. In E. R. Ramey and D. S. O'Doherty (Eds.), *Electrical studies on the unanesthetized brain*. New York: Hoeber, 1960. Pp. 214–242.

Higgens, J. W., Mahl, G. F., Delgado, J. M. R., and Hamlin, H. Behavioral changes during intracerebral electrical stimulation. *Arch. Neurol. Psychiat.*, 1956, **76**, 399–419.

Olds, J. Effects of hunger and male sex hormone on self-stimulation of the brain. *J. comp. physiol. Psychol.*, 1958, **51**, 320–324.

Olds, J.   Differential effects of drives and drugs on self-stimulation at different brain sites.   In D. E. Sheer (Ed.), *Electrical stimulation of the brain*.   Austin: Univ. of Texas Press, 1961. Pp. 350–366.

Olds, J.   Hypothalamic substrates of reward.   *Physiol. Rev.*, 1962, **42**, 554–604.

Olds, J., and Milner, P.   Positive reinforcement produced by electrical stimulation of septal area and other regions of rat brain.   *J. comp. physiol. Psychol.*, 1954, **47**, 419–427.

Sem-Jacobsen, C. W.   Effects of electrical stimulation of human brain.   *Electroencephal. clin. Neurophysiol.*, 1959, **11**, 379. (abstract)

Sem-Jacobsen, C. W., and Torkildsen, A.   Depth recording and electrical stimulation in the human brain.   In E. R. Ramey and D. S. O'Doherty (Eds.), *Electrical studies on the unanesthetized brain*.   New York: Hoeber, 1960. Pp. 275–287.

Stein, L.   Effects and interactions of imipramine, chlorpromazine, reserpine and amphetamine on self-stimulation: Possible neurophysiological basis of depression.   In J. Wortis (Ed.), *Recent advances in biological psychiatry*, Vol. 4.   New York: Plenum Press, 1961. Pp. 288–308.

The preceding four papers have provided some empirical evidence regarding electrical self-stimulation in studying the operation of the brain and of behavior. A considerable amount of evidence based on the use of this technique is now available.

The development of science and scientific understanding, however, requires not only the collection of empirical data but also the integration of data into meaningful frameworks, or theories. In the final article of this section, psychologist Everett W. Bovard attempts to integrate the available data from electrical self-stimulation studies into such a framework. From his theory of positive and negative brain systems, he speculates about effects of early childhood experiences on the developing personality of the child.

THE BALANCE BETWEEN NEGATIVE AND POSITIVE BRAIN SYSTEM ACTIVITY*

Everett W. Bovard

Location and Function of Two Systems

Preliminary evidence for two brain systems concerned with autonomic and neuroendocrine function has been considered previously

* Reprinted from *Perspectives in Biology and Medicine*, Vol. 6, 1962, pp. 116–127. By permission of The University of Chicago Press. Copyright © 1962 by the University of Chicago.

(Bovard, 1961a). The first of these systems, inhibitory with respect to the neuroendocrine response to stress, appears to be strongly represented in the anterior and lateral hypothalamus; the second, facilitatory with respect to the stress response, is strongly represented in the posterior and medial hypothalamus. Self-stimulation in the first of these systems through depth electrodes appears to be rewarding for both man and animal, whereas electrical stimulation in the second system has adverse effects.

The two hypothalamic zones where these systems are represented have been shown to be reciprocally inhibitory, and the hypothesis has been advanced (Bovard, 1961a) that this is but a special case of the general reciprocally inhibitory relationship between these two systems.

Additional evidence from work with man and monkeys now provides a more differentiated view of the structure and function of these two systems. In work with human patients undergoing neurosurgery, Sem-Jacobsen and Torkildsen (1960) found that a positive and a negative system, with opposite reactions to electrical stimulation, are located close to each other in the ventromedial frontal lobe, temporal lobe, parietal lobe, hypothalamus, and midbrain, as well as in more midline regions (not specified).

For example, he found[1] that stimulation of the amygdaloid nucleus of the temporal lobe at one point induced a euphoric reaction in the patient, but at a point 0.5 millimeter away a fear reaction. The responses of both systems appeared to vary together, both being strong or weak in the same region.

Patients stimulated with electrodes in the positive system reported feelings of pleasure and euphoria, and on occasion requested further stimulation (Sem-Jacobsen and Torkildsen, 1960). When allowed to stimulate this system in their own brains, the patients did so on occasion to the point of convulsion. In recording from positive system sites through the same electrodes as used for stimulation, immediately after such stimulation, Sem-Jacobsen found that afterdischarge was still taking place in the microregion that had been stimulated.

In general, Sem-Jacobsen found feelings of ease and relaxation, joy with smiling, and great satisfaction, respectively, to be elicited from stimulation of different areas in the positive system. Negative responses could be subdivided into areas resulting in restlessness, anxiety, depression, fright, and horror. To avoid unnecessary discomfort for the patient, the negative system was stimulated very little in these studies.

[1] C. W. Sem-Jacobsen, personal communication, 1959.

The relaxing and calming effect of ventromedial frontal lobe stimulation was strong enough to terminate psychotic episodes in less than one minute on several occasions, Sem-Jacobsen found. It should be noted here that, of eighteen patients studied in this series, fifteen had been diagnosed as schizophrenic, one as a psychopath, and two were epileptics.

It is interesting to note that when Sem-Jacobsen stimulated two positive areas (ventromedial frontal lobe and central temporal lobe) in rapid succession, he found what he termed a good clinical effect of some duration in calming a rather violent manic patient. The effect of stimulating either one of these areas at separate times was in the same direction but of shorter duration. This suggests that summation of positive system responses may take place.

Depth electrode studies, also with mental patients, over a period of seven years by Heath and his group at Tulane (Heath and Mickle, 1960) present a picture roughly similar to that emerging from Sem-Jacobsen's work but differing in detail. Heath found that patients stimulated in the septal region appeared more alert, spoke more rapidly, and generally reported that they "felt good." Several asked for more such stimulation. Patients with intractable pain obtained immediate relief through such stimulation.

In contrast, electrical stimulation of the rostral hypothalamus[2] by Heath and his group resulted in marked discomfort, with patients complaining of anxiety, evidencing rapid heartbeat, and flushing. Stimulation at sites in the caudal hypothalamus and the tegmentum of the midbrain yielded diffuse tension and rage reactions. All stimulation to the amygdala and anterior hippocampus produced emergency reactions of rage or fear.

The differences between these two sets of findings are not entirely explicable in terms of current parameters. Sem-Jacobsen used a bipolar, biphasic square pulse of 1 millisecond duration, at 60 pulses per second, with amperage ranging from 60 to 500 microamperes. Heath made use of 1-millisecond pulses of alternating polarity in his recent studies, at a rate of 50 pulse-pairs per second, using a current of about 8 to 70 milliamperes. Although shorter pulses required greater cur-

---

[2] A horizontal cross-section of the hypothalamus would show the anterior zone extending laterally in the posterior direction, while the posterior zone extends medially in the anterior direction, on either side of the third ventricle (Bovard, 1961a). Hence, whether an electrode in the rostral or anterior hypothalamus were in the anterior zone and mediating reinforcing and parasympathetic effects, or in the posterior zone and mediating stress effects, would depend on exactly how far from the midline it had been placed.

rent to produce responses similar to longer pulses, as could be expected, Heath found no essential difference in clinical, behavioral, or physiological effects from stimulation of the same structure with different stimulation parameters.

Experimental work on depth electrode stimulation of monkey brains by Lilly (1960), making use of pulse-pairs of opposite polarity with a total duration of about 0.2 millisecond, has shown that the regions yielding reinforcing effects extend, in order of decreasing strength of representation, from the basal tegmentum of the midbrain through the ventromedial nucleus of the hypothalamus, the intralaminar system of the thalamus, the septal area, and the upper fornix to the head of the caudate nucleus and the putamen.

On the basis of this work, the negative system in monkeys appears to be located more caudally in the diencephalon and in the midbrain, where, as noted above, positive system responses are also found.

An extreme point in the negative system, which elicited a state of anxiety and terror more unpleasant even than severe pain for the monkey, was found in the medial hypothalamus just above the pituitary stalk (Bovard, 1961a; Lilly, 1957).

In the circuit set up by Lilly, the monkey had only to touch a metal contact connected with a sensitive condenser. This induced a voltage shift, and as soon as the monkey released his contact, the brain stimulation either started, for positive system stimulation, or stopped, for negative stimulation. If the electrode was in a positive site, the release of the contact triggered a train of a predetermined number of pulse-pairs, irrespective of rate of delivery. If the electrode was in a negative site, releasing the contact shut off a train of stimulation which was delivered to the monkey brain at fixed intervals by an electric timer. Each touch and release only stopped the particular train of stimuli in progress, not the next one in the pretimed sequence.

Except for the apparently reduced extent of the negative system in the monkey, where it appears to be confined to diencephalon and midbrain, the results were basically similar to those obtained in human subjects—and again suggest the presence of two neural systems of opposite function. The long-term effects of positive or negative stimulation on metabolic and psychological functions in the monkey are, however, of particular interest for our purposes.

Lilly found that long-continued stimulation of the positive regions in the monkey brain resulted in a subtle change in the animal's behavior and relationship to the experimenter. The monkey was less jittery, appeared more tractable and more interested in what the observer was doing, and even developed what can be termed as "affectionate" attitude toward the experimenter, such as grooming his hand instead of scratching it (as normally).

In contrast, continued stimulation at negative sites had severe and drastic effects. Three hours of stimulation in the anterior midline hypothalamus [see Footnote 2, p. 128—Ed.], for example, resulted in deleterious aftereffects lasting 24 to 48 hours. The monkey became increasingly jittery and excitable and bit and scratched when approached. He refused to eat, and food already in the stomach was held there, with digestion apparently halted, and was vomited during the night. Skin and mucous membrane were pallid and heart rate was increased. In time, the monkey became apathetic and unresponsive.

Since stimulation in this region has also been shown to trigger a pituitary-adrenal response to stress (Mason, 1958) the picture here appears to represent a generalized response to stress involving sympathetic autonomic, metabolic, and behavioral components.

Exploration of the rat brain through electrical stimulation of the unanesthetized animal by Olds and his co-workers (Olds and Milner, 1954; Olds, 1960) originally suggested that the negative system was limited to an area of the diencephalon and midbrain caudal to the descending fibers of the fornix. A recent study by Wurtz and Olds (1961) has shown, however, that both the positive and negative systems are represented in the amygdaloid nucleus, as the work of Sem-Jacobsen [see Footnote 1, p. 127—Ed.] suggested is the case in the human brain.

In these studies of Olds and his group, positive sites are those where the rat will press a lever in a Skinner box to deliver current to his brain, the rate sometimes reaching 7,000 an hour (interpeduncular nucleus of the tegmentum). Negative sites are those where the rat, having once stimulated himself, will avoid doing so again.

The stimulus used was a sine wave of 60 cycles per second with a current ranging from 5 to 100 microamperes. The stimulus series lasted for 0.5 seconds; if the rat held longer, the current went off and he had to release the lever and press it again. If he pressed the lever for less than 0.5 seconds, the current went off when he let go.

The fundamental discovery of sites in the rat brain where electrical stimulation has rewarding effects was made by Olds in 1953 (Olds and Milner, 1954) while working in Hebb's laboratory at McGill University. This work has proliferated since that time and has now extended to monkey and human brains, as we have seen.

Perhaps the most remarkable aspect of this work in brain stimulation, and certainly the most interesting theoretically, is the reciprocal inhibition found to exist between the positive system, where stimulation results in behavior maintaining reception of the stimulus energy, and the negative system, where stimulation results in behavior disrupting reception of the stimulus energy.

In electrical stimulation of the rat brain, Olds (1960) found that stimulation of the positive or reinforcing system reduced sensitivity to pain, while stimulation of the negative system tended to reduce the effect of stimulation in rewarding areas. This finding of reciprocal inhibition between the two systems has been supported by further work with monkeys.

Lilly (1960) found that stimulation in rewarding areas of the monkey brain could attenuate or even eliminate fearful, angry, and even painlike behavior. Such rewarding stimulation increased the threshold for fear or pain produced by stimulation in the negative system. On the other hand, when the monkey was stimulating himself at sites in the positive system, simultaneous stimulation in negative areas caused him to increase his rate of response, apparently because the negative stimulation had increased the threshold for positive stimuli.

Heath and Mickle (1960) have shown, at the human level, that electrical stimulation of the septal region can provide immediate relief from intractable pain in cancer and rheumatoid arthritis patients, the relief lasting two or three days. Sem-Jacobsen (Brecher and Brecher, 1961) has used daily stimulation in rewarding brain areas of terminal cancer patients to keep them comfortable over a period of months, with only a minimum use of narcotics. This treatment, it should be noted, is suitable only for a few hospitalized patients under special conditions.

For ethical reasons, stimulation of the negative system in human patients has been extremely limited, and the effects of such stimulation on the threshold for reinforcing stimuli in the human brain have not been ascertained.

The available evidence therefore suggests that the positive and negative systems are reciprocally inhibitory. Consequences of this arrangement will be explored below.

In sum, therefore, there is now further evidence for the existence of two reciprocally inhibitory neural systems, extending from the fronto-orbital cortex and temporal pole at the anterior tip of the brain back to midbrain levels. The first of these systems, the Olds reinforcing or positive system, is apparently inhibitory with respect to the neuroendocrine response to stress, mediates parasympathetic function, and, on electrical stimulation, has rewarding effects such that the subject seeks to continue stimulation. The second of these systems, the stress or negative, is facilitatory with respect to the neuroendocrine response to stress, mediates sympathetic autonomic effects, and, on electrical stimulation, has adverse effects such that the subject seeks to discontinue stimulation.

The problem now is, given these indications of the nature of these two systems, what is their psychological and metabolic function? The probable mediation of the reinforcing components of such stimuli as affection, social approval, and handling by the positive system has been considered previously (Bovard, 1961a). It would seem logical that the second system should mediate emotional stress—that is to say, a noxious psychological stimulus that must be mediated by the central nervous system to induce a pituitary-adrenal cortical reaction.

To show that emotional stress is, in fact, mediated by the negative system, it would be necessary to demonstrate that noxious psychological stimuli induce electrical activity at the same sites where electrical stimulation has been found to induce both negative behavioral effects and a rise in plasma corticosteroid level. To demonstrate experimentally that the positive system does mediate rewarding psychological stimuli, it would be necessary to show that such stimuli induce electrical activity at brain sites where electrical stimulation has been shown to have rewarding effects.

The time is now ripe to consider the logical implications of such mediation of reinforcing and noxious stimuli, in view of the reciprocal relationship between these two systems and their final common pathway for influence on the anterior pituitary, the hypothalamus.

Drift to Extremes

Reciprocal inhibition between the two systems would mean that, under activation of the positive system, the threshold for emotional stress would be increased. This follows if we make the reasonable assumption, considered elsewhere (Bovard, 1961b), that level of electrical activity in the negative system is inversely related to the threshold for emotional stress, and if we consider further that activity of the positive system will inhibit activity of the negative by virtue of their reciprocal innervation.

Therefore, any stimulus, physical or psychological, that could be shown to activate the reinforcing system, such as affection or handling, would thereby dampen activity of the negative system under emotional stress. This would have protective effects for the organism in those circumstances where a neuroendocrine response to a psychological stress like a forthcoming doctoral preliminary examination, and its protein catabolic consequences and concomitant effects on thinking and behavior, could be considered inappropriate (Bovard, 1961a).

Conversely, under activation of the negative system, the threshold for reinforcing stimuli would be raised, as Lilly's work with monkeys suggests (1960). This follows if we assume that electrical activity in the reinforcing system is inversely related to the threshold for reinforcing stimuli, and if we further consider that activity of the negative system will inhibit activity of the positive system.

Thus, any noxious stimulus complex, whether physical or psychological, that could be shown to activate the neural negative system would have the effect of dampening the response of the positive system. This would suggest the hypothesis that in a generally threatening environment, reinforcing stimuli would be virtually inoperative. This has interesting implications for treatment of juvenile delinquency and for classroom behavior.

But further, let us consider that the balance between the positive and negative systems is "set" to maintain a low level of stress system activity, as Gellhorn's work (1957) suggests by implication. Under the impact of emotional stress, the threshold for noxious stimuli would be lowered, while the threshold for reinforcing stimuli would be raised. This would mean that the probability of reinforcing stimuli reversing this trend toward an extreme state would continually decrease. Lilly's work with monkeys (1960), noted above, suggests specifically that, after a certain point, rewarding stimulation can no longer halt the apparently self-accelerating trend toward an extreme stress reaction resulting from electrical stimulation in the posterior hypothalamus. Deleterious effects of 3 hours of such stimulation were found to last from 24 to 48 hours, as mentioned.

There are built-in neural and chemical mechanisms to halt an extreme response to emotional stress. The hippocampal-fornix system has been shown in monkeys to dampen the pituitary-adrenal response to prolonged emotional stress (Mason et al., 1960). Higher blood levels of adrenocorticotropic hormone (ACTH) (Kitay, Holub, and Jailer, 1959) and of adrenal cortical hormones (Péron and Dorfman, 1959), which could be expected to result from emotional stress, have been shown to inhibit further release of ACTH from the pituitary. Lilly's work suggests, however, that these mechanisms are not always effective under extreme stimulation of the negative system.

These considerations therefore suggest that under emotional stress there is a built-in tendency for the positive-negative system complex, taken as a whole, to drift into a state of extreme negative system dominance.

While there would be a similar tendency for the total system, under rewarding stimulation, to drift into a state of extreme reinforcing system dominance (since the threshold for reinforcing stimuli would be lowered while the threshold for noxious stimuli would be raised), with feelings of euphoria at the human level, this tendency would not be so pronounced, since the positive-negative system complex is apparently set genetically to favor the stressward drift (Gellhorn, 1957).

The euphoric feelings that often follow relief from a severe stress (exhilaration after combat, elation on pulling away from a sinking ship) can be accounted for if we assume that, under extreme stress, inhibition of the positive system is only a first phase that is followed by increased activity of the positive system to counterbalance the protein catabolic and other consequences of extreme negative system activity. That is to say, under long-continued stress, we may consider the possibility that some normal balance between, for example, sympathetic and parasympathetic output to the viscera has to be maintained by counteractivity of the positive system, even in the absence of external reinforcing stimulation.[3] When the stress is suddenly withdrawn, the positive system maintains its hyperactivity longer than the negative system, and, therefore, feelings of elation and general euphoria may be experienced.

Such a balance between the positive and negative systems, where both are hyperactive, must be considered highly unstable compared to the normal resting level balance.

Setting the Balance

In the normal case, the resting level balance between the positive and negative systems would determine the probability that a neutral stimulus will trigger a pituitary-adrenal reaction—that is to say, the threshold for emotional stress (Bovard, 1961b). This balance would therefore determine the rate of expenditure of the organism's metabolic reserves in response to environmental stimuli.

Setting this balance would appear to be a function of the amygdala, a small nuclear mass situated in the dorsomedial portion of the

---

[3] It would appear probable that one function of sexual stimuli in severe stress is to initiate such counteractivity of the positive system and, hence, temporarily restore a semblance of the normal balance between output of the two systems.

temporal lobe, in front of and partly above the tip of the inferior horn.

Herrick suggested in 1932 (Herrick, 1933) that the function of the olfactory cortex, of which the amygdala is an element, is to discriminate between noxious and desirable stimuli, to activate appropriate sensory-motor systems, and to serve as a nonspecific activator for cortical and subcortical systems by means of facilitatory and inhibitory mechanisms. This description of function can be applied to the amygdala alone, on the basis of available evidence (Gloor, 1960). Both the positive and negative systems are represented in the amygdala of man [see Footnote 1, p. 127—Ed.] and the rat (Wurtz and Olds, 1961), and the amygdala has a rich projection to the hypothalamus by two separate routes: the familiar stria terminalis and the recently discovered (Klingler and Gloor, 1960) ventral amygdaloid tract. The hypothalamus, as we have suggested, is the final common pathway for the influence of the positive and negative systems on the anterior pituitary.

Release of ACTH from the anterior pituitary above the resting level, and, hence, release of adrenal cortical hormones like hydrocortisone in the human and corticosterone in the rat, would depend on the balance of activity between the positive and negative systems and the resultant neural output to the region of the median eminence (Bovard, 1961a). This balance would appear to be determined by amygdaloid influence.

In exactly the same way, the activity of a single anterior horn cell in the spinal cord, its output to a muscle fiber or group of fibers, depends on the balance between excitatory and inhibitory influences impinging on it from the long corticospinal and extrapyramidal pathways, this balance probably being influenced by the cerebellum.

The hypothesis that the amygdala differentiates alarming from reinforcing stimuli through conditioning of its activity to environmental stimuli, and that it activates the appropriate response system in each case, is supported by the fact that experimental amygdaloid lesions in monkeys (Weiskrantz, 1956) make it extremely difficult for this animal to identify motivationally relevant stimuli. The neurophysiological mechanisms by which the amygdala could make such discriminations, despite its lack of somatotopographical organization, have been described by Gloor.[4]

If the amygdala sets the normal balance between the reinforcing and stress systems, it is quite conceivable that this balance is set in

[4] P. Gloor, unpublished paper, University of Virginia, 1959.

favor of the positive system in domesticated species and more in favor of the negative system in wild species. It would follow that removal of the amygdala would have opposite effects in wild and domesticated species.

This would account for the apparently contradictory findings that amygdalectomy in the dog increases pituitary-adrenal activity (Martin et al., 1958) while it has a delayed and precisely opposite effect in the monkey (Mason et al., 1960). Amygdalectomy should, therefore, produce an increase in emotional reactivity in laboratory rats but a decrease in wild rats of the same species.

These considerations suggest that the relative balance between the two great neural systems of the brain, the positive system and the negative system, is determined genetically and by early experience, probably under modulation of the amygdala.

Some Further Speculations

A simple hypothesis to account for the effects of maternal deprivation (Bowlby, 1951) is that lack of stimulation of the positive system in the first months of life permanently alters the balance between negative and positive systems in favor of the former. A permanently lower threshold for emotional stress would result (Bovard, 1961a). Hence, a greater expenditure of metabolic reserves in response to environmental change would leave depleted resources to deal with disease and injury. Thus, maternally-deprived children should be less resistant to infectious disease, as the work of Spitz (1946) suggests may be the case. Relevant here is the finding that mice subjected to emotional stress are more susceptible to herpes simplex (Rasmussen et al., 1957).

The effects of maternal deprivation in inducing negative system dominance would include not only a lower threshold for emotional stress, but also a higher threshold for reinforcing stimuli, since positive system activity would be inhibited. Therefore, such maternally-deprived individuals should show a reduced capacity for response to such reinforcing stimuli as affection or social approval. It would be more difficult to reach them by these means.

Finally, the effect of post-weaning handling (21 to 43 days) in increasing viability of the laboratory rat under stress (Bovard, 1958) can be accounted for on the hypothesis that such stimulation induces a permanent imbalance in favor of positive system activity, resulting in a higher threshold for stress and therefore conservation and storage of metabolic resources in the face of environmental change. Long's findings[5] that handled rats survive starvation an average of 53.8 hours longer than unhandled controls of the same weight is worth noting here.

REFERENCES

Bovard, E. W.   The effects of early handling on viability of the albino rat.   *Psychol. Rev., 1958,* **65,** 257–271.

Bovard, E. W.   A concept of hypothalamic functioning.   *Perspect. Biol. Med.,* 1961, **5,** 52–60.   (a)

Bovard, E. W.   A note on the threshold for emotional stress.   *Psychol. Rev.,* 1961, **68,** 216–218.   (b)

Bowlby, J.   *Maternal care and mental health.*   Geneva: World Health Org., 1951.

Brecher, R., and Brecher, E.   Happiest creatures on earth?   *Harper's Magazine,* 1961 (April), **222** (1331), 85–90.

Gellhorn, E.   *Autonomic imbalance and the hypothalamus.*   Minneapolis: Univ. of Minnesota Press, 1957.

Gloor, P.   Amygdala.   In J. Field (Ed.), *Handbook of physiology,* Sect. 1, Vol. 2.   Washington, D.C.: American Physiological Soc., 1960. Pp. 1395–1420.

Heath, R. G., and Mickle, W. A.   Evaluation of seven years' experience with depth electrode studies in human patients.   In E. R. Ramey and D. S. O'Doherty (Eds.), *Electrical studies on the unanesthetized brain.* New York: Hoeber, 1960. Pp. 214–242.

Herrick, C. J.   Functions of olfactory parts of cerebral cortex.   *Proc. Natl. Acad. Sci.,* 1933, **19,** 7–14.

Kitay, J. I., Holub, D. A., and Jailer, J. W.   Inhibition of pituitary ACTH release: An extra-adrenal action of exogenous ACTH.   *Endocrinology,* 1959, **64,** 475–482.

Klingler, J., and Gloor, P.   The connections of the amygdala and of the anterior temporal cortex in the human brain.   *J. comp. Neurol.,* 1960, **115,** 333–369.

Lilly, J. C.   True primary emotional state of anxiety-terror-panic in contrast to a "sham" emotion or "pseudo-affective" state evoked by stimulation of hypothalamus.   *Feder. Proc.,* 1957, **16,** 81. (abstract)

Lilly, J. C.   Learning motivated by subcortical stimulation: The "start" and the "stop" patterns of behavior.   In E. R. Ramey and D. S. O'Doherty (Eds.), *Electrical studies on the unanesthetized brain.* New York: Hoeber, 1960. Pp. 78–103.

Martin, J., Endroczi, E., and Bata, G.   Effect of the removal of amygdalic nuclei on the secretion of adrenal cortical hormones.   *Acta Physiol. Acad. Sci. Hung.,* 1958, **14,** 131–134.

Mason, J. W.   Plasma 17-hydrocorticosteroid response to hypothalamic stimulation in the conscious rhesus monkey.   *Endocrinology,* 1958, **63,** 403–411.

[5] H. G. Long, M.A. thesis, University of Toronto, 1955.

Mason, J. W., Nauta, W. J. H., Brady, J. V., Robinson, J. A., and Thach, J. S., Jr.   Limbic system influences on the pituitary-adrenal cortical system.   *Psychosom. Med.*, 1960, **22**, 322. (abstract)

Olds, J.   Differentiation of reward systems in the brain by self-stimulation techniques.   In E. R. Ramey and D. S. O'Doherty (Eds.), *Electrical studies on the unanesthetized brain.*   New York: Hoeber, 1960. Pp. 17–49.

Olds, J., and Milner, P.   Positive reinforcement produced by electrical stimulation of septal area and other regions of rat brain.   *J. comp. physiol. Psychol.*, 1954, **47**, 419–427.

Péron, F. G., and Dorfman, R. I.   A method for the evaluation of adrenocorticotropic hormone suppressing action of corticoids.   *Endocrinology*, 1959, **64**, 431–436.

Rasmussen, A. F., Jr., Marsh, J. T., and Brill, N. Q.   Increased susceptibility to herpes simplex in mice subjected to avoidance-learning stress or restraint.   *Proc. Soc. exp. Biol. Med.*, 1957, **96**, 183–189.

Sem-Jacobsen, C. W., and Torkildsen, A.   Depth recording and electrical stimulation in the human brain.   In E. R. Ramey and D. S. O'Doherty (Eds.), *Electrical studies on the unanesthetized brain.*   New York: Hoeber, 1960. Pp. 275–287.

Spitz, R. A.   Hospitalism: A follow-up report on investigation described in Volume I, 1945.   *Psychoanal. Stud. Child*, 1946, **2**, 113–117.

Weiskrantz, L.   Behavioral changes associated with ablation of amygdaloid complex in monkeys.   *J. comp. physiol. Psychol.*, 1956, **49**, 381–391.

Wurtz, R. H., and Olds, J.   Chronic stimulation of amygdaloid complex.   *Feder. Proc.*, 1961, **20**, 336. (abstract)

SUGGESTIONS FOR
ADVANCED READING

Olds, J.   Hypothalamic substrates of reward.   *Physiol. Rev.*, 1962, **42**, 554–604.

Ramey, E. R., and O'Doherty, D. S. (Eds.).   *Electrical studies on the unanesthetized brain.*   New York: Hoeber, 1960.

Sheer, D. E. (Ed.).   *Electrical stimulation of the brain.*   Austin: Univ. of Texas Press, 1961.

GLOSSARY

Acquisition. Gaining, adding, or incorporating something on the part of an organism; or that which is gained. For psychology the term is a loose synonym for learning or maturation, or both.

Adenylic acid. A nucleic acid yielding adenine on decomposition.

Adipsia. Absence of thirst. Condition in which an animal consumes no water.

Adrenergic drugs. Drugs whose action on the central nervous system is similar to that of adrenaline (epinephrine).

Androgens. Hormones, secreted in both sexes but more abundantly in males, that influence the development of maleness, either of structure or behavior.

Anhedonic. Adjective referring to absence of pleasure or unpleasure where normally expected.

Antidromic. Conduction of nerve impulses in a direction opposite to the normal.

Bipolar. Having processes at both ends or poles, as in bipolar nerve cells.

Buccal. Pertaining to the mouth cavity.

Carbachol. A cholinergic drug.

Catheterized. Having a catheter (tube) inserted into particular area to permit injection or withdrawal of fluids.

Caudal. Directed toward the tail end of the body.

Cholinergic drugs. Drugs whose action on the central nervous system is similar to that of acetylcholine.

Columnar epithelium. Epithelium consisting of, or having the superficial layer composed of, tall, narrow, more or less cylindrical cells; as in the human digestive tract.

Cytidylic acid. A nucleic acid yielding cytosine on decomposition.

Deglutition. The act or process of swallowing.

Desiccation. Extreme dryness.

Diabetes insipidus. A metabolic disorder, marked by great thirst and the passage of large quantities of urine with no excess of sugar.

Diuresis. Increased secretion of urine.

Dorsal. Denoting a position toward the back; same as *posterior* in human anatomy.

Electroencephalography. The recording of the electric currents developed in the brain, by means of electrodes applied to the scalp, directly to the surface of the brain, or within the tissue of various regions of the brain.

Epigastrium. Abdominal surface overlying the stomach.

Epithelium. A membranous cellular tissue that lines a cavity of an animal body.

Extinction. The progressive reduction in the conditioned response consequent upon either of two experimental procedures: (a) the repeated presentation of the CS without the UCS; or (b) the withholding of reward after the emission of a conditioned instrumental response.

Fistula. A tube or other opening leading to an internal hollow organ.

Glossopharyngeal nerve. Ninth cranial nerve; innervates the mucous membrane and a muscle of the throat (pharynx), a salivary gland, and the mucous membrane of the posterior third of the tongue for taste.

Glucagon. A hyperglycemic-glycogenalytic factor thought to be secreted by the pancreas in response to hypoglycemia or to stimulation by the growth hormone of the anterior pituitary.

Guanylic acid. A nucleic acid yielding guanine on decomposition.

Hypertonic. A solution more concentrated than the system (e.g., blood) with which it is compared.

Hypophysis. The pituitary gland: composed of two main lobes, anterior and posterior, which produce different groups of hormones. Often referred to as the "master gland."

Hypothalamus. A small group of nuclei lying below the thalamus in the midbrain, thought to be involved in motivation of the organism as well as being a motor-reflex control center.

Hypotonic. A solution less concentrated than the system (e.g., blood) with which it is compared.

Intraperitoneally. Within the peritoneum (abdominal cavity or "gut"). Used with reference to place of injection.

Isotonic. A solution having the same concentration as the system (e.g., blood) with which it is compared.

Lingual nerves. Nerves innervating the tongue.

Microampere. One millionth of an ampere.

Microgram. One millionth of a gram.

Milliliter. One thousandth of a liter; equal to 1 cubic centimeter.

Millisecond. One thousandth of a second.

Mucosa. Mucous membrane.

NaCl. Sodium chloride; common table salt.

Noradrenaline. Norepinephrine. A hormone similar to adrenaline produced by the adrenal glands. May also be involved in synaptic transmission of nerve impulses in the autonomic nervous system.

Nucleic acid. Any of a group of acids occurring in organic nuclear material and consisting of a combination of phosphoric acid with a carbohydrate and a base. Currently thought to be responsible for genetic transfer.

Nucleotide. One of the compounds into which nucleic acid is divided by the action of a nuclease.

Operational definition. Definition of a concept in terms of the operations used to measure it. For example, "intelligence" may be operationally defined as a score on a particular intelligence test.

Optic chiasm. Area where optic nerves partially cross.

Osmosis. The tendency of a fluid to pass through a semipermeable membrane, e.g., the wall of a living cell, into a solution of lower concentration, so as to equalize concentrations on both sides of the membrane.

Osmotic pressure. The pressure produced by osmosis.

Perifornical region. Area near the fornix.

pH. A symbol for the hydrogen ion concentration; or acidity-alkalinity balance, in a liquid: 7.0 is neutral, less is acid, more is alkaline.

Pharyngeal. Adjective referring to the pharynx: part of the throat between mouth and esophagus.

Pitressin. Vasopressin; one of the two hormones of the posterior pituitary. It raises the blood pressure by stimulating the contraction of the muscular tissue of the capillaries and arterioles. It contracts the intestinal musculature and increases peristalsis.

Pituitary. *See* Hypophysis.

Polydipsia. Excessive thirst. Condition in which an animal consumes excess quantities of water.

Polyurea. Profuse urination.

Psychogenic. Having a psychic origin; originating in mental or emotional conflict.

Pyrogenicity. Ability to produce fever.

Rhinencephalon. The olfactory or smell brain, thought to be involved in emotion as well as in olfaction.

Ribonucleic acid. Compound of nucleic acids and ribose involved in the formation of protein in the developing organism.

RNA. Ribonucleic acid.

Rostral. Directed toward the front end of the body.

Squamous epithelium. Stratified epithelium that consists in its outer layers of small scale-like cells, as in the epidermis of the human skin.

Stereotaxic. Adjective describing an instrument for fixing the head position of an animal under anesthesia so that electrodes may be accurately inserted.

Telencephalon. End brain; including cerebral cortex, corpus striatum, and rhinencephalon.

Teleosts. Fishes with a bony rather than a cartilaginous skeleton, including most jawed fishes.

Testosterone. Androgenic (male) hormone.

Uridylic acid. A nucleic acid yielding uracil on decomposition.

Vagus nerve. Tenth cranial nerve; innervates the mucous membrane of the pharynx and larynx and the muscles of these organs. Also has a complex distribution to viscera.

Ventral. Denoting a position toward the front or belly; same as *anterior* in human anatomy.

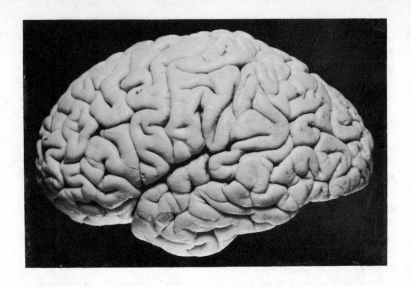

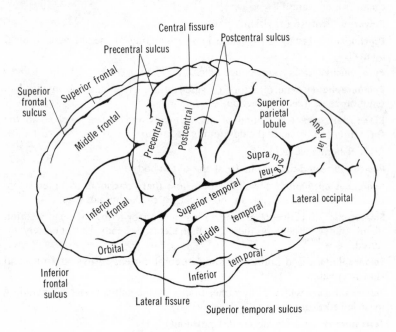

Photograph and sketch of the lateral surface of the human brain. The arachnoid and pia mater have been removed. (Brain photographs and sketches from E. Gardner, Fundamentals of Neurology, *4th ed. Philadelphia: W. B. Saunders Company, 1963.)*

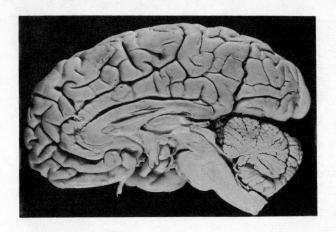

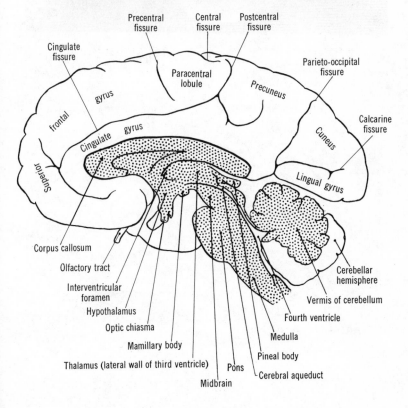

Precentral fissure

Central fissure

Postcentral fissure

Cingulate fissure

Paracentral lobule

Precuneus

Parieto-occipital fissure

frontal gyrus

Cingulate gyrus

Cuneus

Calcarine fissure

Superior

Lingual gyrus

Corpus callosum

Olfactory tract

Interventricular foramen

Hypothalamus

Optic chiasma

Mamillary body

Thalamus (lateral wall of third ventricle)

Pons

Midbrain

Cerebral aqueduct

Pineal body

Medulla

Fourth ventricle

Vermis of cerebellum

Cerebellar hemisphere

Photograph of a brain sectioned in the median plane and sketch of the medial surface.